SHETLAND PONIES
FROM
SHETLAND

SHETLAND PONIES
FROM
SHETLAND

Margaret Hunter

Published by
The Shetland Times Ltd.,
Lerwick, Shetland.
2000

Shetland Ponies from Shetland
Copyright © Margaret Hunter, 2000

ISBN 1 898852 66 9

First published by The Shetland Times Ltd., 2000

Cover design © Nicolas Barnham

Margaret Hunter has asserted her right under the
Copyright, Designs and Patents Act 1988 to be
identified as author of this work.

British Library Cataloguing-in-Publication Data
A catalogue record for this book is available from the British Library.

Printed and published by
The Shetland Times Ltd.,
Prince Alfred Street, Lerwick,
Shetland ZE1 0EP, Scotland.

For my family

CONTENTS

ACKNOWLEDGEMENTS

I would like to thank all the people who have so readily helped to find information over the past two years and those who have lent photographs. I am grateful to Miss Jem Anderson, Mrs Marie Brooker, Mrs Lorna Burgess, Mr Tom Burgess, Mr Dennis Coutts and Mr John Coutts, Mrs Kathleen Ewan, Mrs Myrna Flaws, Mrs Wendy Gear, Mr Leslie Henderson, Mrs Margaret Hughson, Mr George Hunter, Mrs Cathy Jamieson, Mr Arthur Laurenson, Mrs Lauraine Manson, Mrs Beth Mead, Mr Bertie Nicolson, Mrs Janice Priest, Mr David Robertson, Ms Valerie Russell, Miss I.D.J. Sandison, Miss Eva Smith, Mr Brian Smith and Mr Angus Johnson of the Shetland Archives, Mr Bill Spence, Mrs May Sutherland of Unst Heritage Centre, Mrs Helen Thomson, Miss Val Turner and Miss Barbara Wilson.

I wish to thank also Aberdeen University Library for permission to print the Washington Wilson photographs, the Shetland Museum for permission to print photographs, my family for their encouragement and especially Alison Hunter for her careful work.

Thanks to The Shetland Times Ltd. for permission to publish various extracts and for publishing *Shetland Ponies from Shetland*.

Cover picture was drawn by Nicholas F.A. Barnham and cover graphics by Reuben Barnham.

PREFACE

Much has been written this century about the Shetland pony by many knowledgeable people and most of us addicts refer to these works again and again. So, you may ask, why another book on the Shetland pony ?

This book came about almost by accident. When it was mooted some three years prior to the millennium that a special celebration should be held in the islands that summer, I felt it would be apt to have a leaflet or booklet concerned mainly with the breed's history in Shetland itself.

Some time later a chance conversation with Jan Sandison concerning the same brought me into contact with the wealth of information contained in the Sandison papers and in particular, the letters to and from Alexander Sandison who bred and dealt in ponies from the late 1850s until his death in 1900. I cannot thank Jan enough for her organisation, unstinting help and enthusiasm. After looking at one batch of letters the "leaflet" quickly disappeared and thoughts of a book emerged.

This book is published this millennium year as a celebration of at least four thousand years of breeding Shetland ponies in the Shetland Isles, making use, as far as possible, of previously untapped and unpublished material.

CHAPTER ONE

ARCHAEOLOGICAL EVIDENCE

Perhaps the time will come when we will be able to say with certainty when the first pony arrived in Shetland but in the meantime we can only speculate and stick to the evidence that we have.

THE NEOLITHIC AGE

Several Neolithic dwellings have been found in Shetland. It is believed that these dwellings belonged to Shetland's earliest settlers, around 2000 BC. In the archaeological book, *The Northern Isles* edited by Dr F. T. Wainwright, C.S.T. Calder describes the results of the excavations of a Neolithic house at the Ness of Gruting where some six hundred relics were found, perfectly preserved under a dense layer of peat ash almost two feet deep.

Among the relics were many animal bones including those of horse, ox, sheep, pig and dog. A quantity of barley was also found there and this has been recently carbon dated as 2000 BC. The growing of barley would further add to the evidence that the climate of the islands has deteriorated considerably since then. This deterioration in the climate which brought more violent gales would have increased the islands' isolation.

When we consider how animals can adapt to their environment over a few generations, as has happened to various species in the Galapagos Islands for example, is it any wonder that the genes of the Shetland pony are so well fixed, given the long periods of isolation it must have experienced during at least four thousand years of development on these windswept islands?

It is interesting to note that while marrow bones of cattle and sheep have often been found split, for the extraction of their nutritious marrow, no split pony bones have ever been found in Shetland. This would point to the horse as a domesticated animal used for transport rather than one hunted for food at least since the Neolithic Age.

THE BRONZE AGE

Our next archaeological evidence comes from the Bronze Age finds at Jarlshof.

Jarlshof, an archaeological site near the airport at Sumburgh was first discovered in 1897. Its excavation was carried on over a period of over fifty years and it became apparent that it was of National and International importance, covering as it did a succession of human occupation from Bronze Age to the early 17th century.

This attractive site with its natural advantages of plenty of good flat building stone, a harbour, comparatively good grazing and a supply of fresh water, first attracted settlers from Orkney at the end of the Late Stone Age, about 2000 BC. Of interest to us are the deposits of animal bones left by these settlers.

1

The Late Margery I. Platt, M.S.C. of the Royal Scottish Museum, Edinburgh, was largely responsible for identifying the bones of the early periods and she found that from the Late Bronze Age, approximately 6th century to the 1st century BC, the animals of food value were most numerous, especially sheep and oxen, as may have been expected. Next in numerical importance were pony, pig, bird, fish, shellfish, seal, walrus and dog. The remains of ponies were scattered throughout the levels. Bone measurements compare favourably with those of the Shetland pony as we know it and it is therefore probable that they belong to this type.

THE BROCH ERA

The broch at Jarlshof is thought to have been built in the 1st century AD and J.R.C. Hamilton states that shortly after its erection "these native people settled in the attached courtyard, living in large round houses of which only one remains. They kept cattle, sheep, pigs and an occasional dog and pony; fished in the tideway off the headland, hunted seal and caught a variety of wild fowl for the cooking pot." At the broch of Clickimin also numerous pony remains have been found.

Following the Broch builders Shetland was peopled largely by the Picts from approximately 300 AD until the arrival of the Vikings in the 8th century. The Picts have proved to be an elusive race with their peculiar language, *Ogham*, yet to be deciphered. They have left many symbol stones in both Orkney and Shetland.

Folk memory speaks of "da peerie folk" or "da Paets" and many believe that those that survived the Viking invasion literally "went underground" and lived on for a time in isolated areas. Their night-time forays, in desperate attempts to survive, could have given rise to many of the old "trowie" stories that abound in Shetland

The Papil Stone.

folklore. There is, for example, a cavern on the east side of Burrafirth known as "da Pettasmog" (the Picts' hiding place).

During the time of the Picts, missionaries or priests arrived from Iona and Ireland. They wore robes and were known as the Papae. Their abodes were named by the Scandinavians, Papa Stur, Papil and Papilsflot for example. It is the Papae that appear on the beautifully carved Papil Stone, one of them seated on the smart looking pony with a pretty head. This stone dates from the 9th century.

From a similar date comes the Bressay stone also depicting a rider on horseback. Although it is of rougher artistry it gives an idea of proportion of rider to pony. These appear to be native ponies.

At Jarlshof the remains of what is believed to be the 9th Century equine relics were much less numerous. Teeth were not often present but various other skeletal parts in a fragmented state occurred. The ponies represented were not of large size, but exceeded the very small breeds in Shetland today. They were generally of adult animals and may well have been the result of the early attempted crosses which the Viking warriors tried out with the stallions that they rode into battle and the native ponies that they found in Shetland

Again in the 11th century and 13th century layers fragmentary relics were found of the slightly bigger skeleton, and also a hitch up point for a pony was found outside a house.

A small bronze figurine of a horse was found at the site of Cross Kirk, Eshaness. Professor Brøgger identified it as a Scandinavian scale-weight from the early 14th century.

With so many unexcavated sites in Shetland, who knows what archaeological finds and information may yet be unearthed to add to our knowledge.

The Bressay Stone.

CHAPTER TWO

WRITTEN EVIDENCE

The exact origin of the Shetland pony is, as yet, unknown, but because it has been bred in the islands for at least four thousand years in comparative isolation its genes are well and truly fixed and it is recognised as the purest of the native breeds.

It is possible that the original Shetland is a mixture of ancient equine stock. Professor H. F. Osbourne of New York, Professor W. Ridgeway of Cambridge and Professor J. C. Ewart of Edinburgh have all put forth their beliefs that there are several lines, possibly five, leading back to the original ancient breeds of horses. Their theories have been well expounded in previous publications.

THE VIKING ERA

Early written evidence is scant. When the Vikings arrived in the 8th century with their aptitude for accurate description, they named everything in sight – hills, rocks, bays, swamps and valleys – in a remarkably detailed manner. A large proportion of these names have survived and among them are many bearing the old Norse **hestr** – **horse**, indicating that there was a concentration of horses in that particular place. These names include:

> Hestakam – horse hill
> da Hestalis – the horses' slope
> Hestanes – horses' promontory
> Hestateng and Hestatong – horses' tongue of land
> Hestneseter – horses' summer pasture
> Hestengert – horses' enclosure
> Hestaford – horses' bay
> Hestigarth – horses' farm
> Hestingot – horses' path
> Hestigio – horses' gio. Like many Shetlandic words there is no apt
> English equivalent. A gio is a cleft in a cliff (sort of).

As far as gleaning any information from the sagas is concerned the results were disappointing. The writers were far more concerned with recording brave deeds, acts of treachery or bloody battles than they were with everyday life or farming issues. There is however one interesting paragraph in *Njal's Saga* which has two relevant points as far as the Shetland connection is concerned.

In Iceland, in the year 1012, on returning home from the Althing (their parliament) a group of men riding east to Myrdale met a man leading a horse carrying peat panniers. This would be the same, or similar to the Shetland method of "flitting" peats but we don't know where the idea originated. It also shows how common the transversing between the islands had become when he goes on to say: "There he arranged a passage with Koblein the Black, an Orcadian, an old friend and a very brave man, who sailed to Shetland and married there. Ari married in Shetland and was the decendant of Einar the Shetlander, a very brave man."

It is quite likely that the piebald gene came from the Icelandic horse and from the piebald it was a short step to the tremendous variety of skewbald colours.

There is no doubt that the Vikings rode their stallions into battle. They also used them for fighting – setting one against the other and goading them on with their sticks. This apparently got out of hand occasionally as tempers flared. They kept a mare or two on the sidelines, for good measure, to keep the stallions in fighting form.

Given the high esteem in which the Norse held their horses it would be natural for them to bring some with them when they settled here and just as natural for them to cross their stallions with the native ponies. The finds at Jarlshof of slightly larger pony remains from the Viking era would bear this out.

Cross ponies pull an Oliver Plough at Fladdabister.   © *Shetland Museum*

This crossing with larger animals would only have worked where there was sufficient food to sustain the results – in areas such as Sumburgh, for instance where the pasture was richer. This was probably the reason also why the Fetlar experiment succeeded many years later when Sir Arthur Nicolson introduced his lovely Arab. Not for nothing has Fetlar been called the "garden of Shetland" and so it could support the work ponies of eleven to thirteen hands as well as its' pure bred ponies.

However these cross breeding trials did not have a lasting effect. The Shetland climate with its frequent gales and driving rain saw to that. In harsh winters, and there were many, only the compact, tougher type of pony would survive; ones with well developed protective coats (so well described in Valerie Russell's book) and ponies with the native cunning to seek shelter and forage for food from hillside or seashore would pull through. This "survival of the fittest" ethic has ensured the hardiness that we find today.

It must be remembered too that the crofters seldom had enough fodder to feed their ponies in winter. The crofter simply had to keep his cows alive to provide milk for the family and butter to sell. Often, in early spring, the cows would be "in lifting" i.e. would be so weak that they had to be hoisted up each morning by a canvas sling until the grass at last appeared and the cattle could stagger out to take advantage of it. In this situation the ponies just had to take their chance.

PROVERBIALLY SURE-FOOTED

Until approximately one hundred and fifty years ago the only means of transport in the Shetland Islands was by boat or pony. There were no roads except in and around Lerwick. However, following several poor harvests in the 1840s the Government, to avoid widespread starvation, began a scheme of road building where the people they employed were paid in meal. To this day some of these roads are referred to as the "meal roads".

The terrain was notoriously rough and boggy so it was important that the ponies were reliable. Local writers seldom remarked on travelling on horseback because, I presume, it was such a common everyday occurrence, but visitors who did leave a record of their journeys through the islands usually comment on the stamina of their sure-footed mounts and those who were accustomed to travelling by horseback frequently praise the strength of the ponies in relation to their small size.

1500s

As early as 1568 Ubaldini comments on their tiny stature and strength.

In 1576, Laurence Bruce of Cultemalindie who built Muness Castle was oppressing the people of Shetland to the brink of destitution. He travelled throughout the Islands with a band of followers and servants and billeted them on people till their provisions were finished. He demanded also, boats and horses for their transport as required. In Brian Smith and John Ballantyne's book *Shetland Documents 1195-1579* it states that Bruce would order "all the parochinaris to cum with thair horssis and boitis to fure him, And albeit that thair cum horsis and boitis sufficient to staik him and his companie, yit gif ony man beis absent with thair horss or boit, he causis poynd thame for xls Yetland payment, for the quhilk he takis up thre dolouris."

Also, a boats' crew that had been "requisitioned" to take Laurence and his followers from Collafirth to Yell arrived later than he wanted and so he had fines imposed upon them ranging from some "gud clayth quhilk, suld have been (for) his wyff ane kirtill" from Williame in Clodasetter to "ane horss from Olaw in Houle".

1600s

In the early sixteen hundreds several people were taken to court for cutting the tails of their neighbours ponies. Horsehair was widely used for fishing lines so was in great demand. Cutting tails was regarded as a serious crime for it left the pony very vulnerable to the elements.

About this time according to Gordon Donaldson in his book *Shetland Life under Earl Patrick,* the majority of people had at least one pony and "even a poor woman like Agnes Olasdochter Aithsting, whose total estate was worth only £20,3s and 4d, had a half share in a mare. It was not uncommon for wealthier families to own half a dozen or more."

There is a letter in the British Library from Earl Patrick to Prince Henry, son of James VI/I, written in October 1609 when Earl Patrick was in prison. He says that he had intended to send Henry two Shetland ponies, but they had become "lame and crookit" in the passage to Edinburgh.

Another crime that was common was riding another man's pony. For example in 1602: "Magnus Dale was found by the Lawting to have ridden a mare of Jerome Tait, without his leave, over four scattalds, and was fined four times 40s." (A given amount for each scattald over which the pony was ridden.)

In Yell there was a theft of a "lymit meiris skin" so lime must have been used for the process of curing skins.

Court at Uyeasound – 8th July, 1617:

> Mr Gilbert Gray, merchant, being convened before the sheriff depute at instance of James Synnens, writer and clerk in the 'wachtership', (guard-ship) for a horse received by James from Walter Gray in Unst, pertaining to Mr Gilbert, alleged given by him to said James, which he referred to his oath of verity, said Gilbert being present made faith that he 'gave' him nocht the said horse but that the wreat only to the said Walter to deliver the said horse to the said James to be transported to him home to Holland to the said Mr Gilbert, and asked instruments.

This is probably the earliest evidence of an export.

Early 1600s – Among the Country Acts of Shetland were several concerning horses.

In 1617 wild horses came under scrutiny:

> thair sal be na wyld horsis kepit conforme to ane act maid of befoir, and that na man sall put thair horses without dykis uncloggit [41r] in tyme cuming fra the last day of May to the tyme the cornes be put in the yeard, under the paine of 40s, toties quoties (as often as it happens) as thay sal be apprehendit or takin in the contrar.

It would appear from the following act that horse owning was almost compulsary for landowners:

> Item ratifeis the act anent boittis and boitis hyris and everie man that ownes six merk land sall have horsis for serving his majesteis lieges upoun their ressonabill expensis, under the paine of 40s, toties quoties.

7

Sir Walter Scott's *The Pirate* gave the impression that the ponies in Shetland were wild and ownerless, but that was not the case, for each was marked before being let loose on the common or scattald. In the early 17th century any ponies for which no owner could be found were claimed by Earl Patrick. He never missed a trick.

From the Smyth of Methven collection in the National Archives comes a description of six Shetland ponies with their earmarks. It is written in 1640 by Andrew Smyth, an Orcadian who was collecting rents in Shetland, to his brother Patrik who was to receive the ponies:

> Sex Yetland naigis sent to Orknay with Hew Dinnisone upon the barron of Brughis boat, to be delyverit to Patrik Smyth of Braco, of the ages, cullouris and markis as followis, 12 August 1640.
>
> 1. [Meall in margin] Ane din naig of 7 yeir ald bygane with ane bit out of ilk lug out of the rycht lug befoir and left behind, both abone.
>
> 2. [Wigga in margin] Ane broun naig of that age, with ane bit befoir on the rycht lug, and a sheir mark on the left.
>
> 3. [Gra*** in margin] Ane blk naig of 4 yeir auld bygane with a bit on hid rycht *** behind and a holl in his left.
>
> 4. Ane uther blak naig of that age, with a bit befoir on his rycht lug and a bit behind on his left.
>
> 5. [Wigga in margin] Ane broun naig of thrie yeir auld with a bit behind and ane befoir on his rycht lug, with a blunt sheir mark on the left.
>
> 6. Ane uther broun litle naig of that age, both his luggis croppit off aboue.
>
> All thir naigis ar markit on the hippis with this mark : PS.
>
> And ar directit to be delyverit to Oliver and Henrie Rowsyis at Rothisholme until the boat come for them.

1700s

In 1774 Low, on a moor at the back of the town of Lerwick, observed a number of people each holding a Sheltie or two. "These" he says, "come daily to Lerwick while the fleet continues, and make a good deal of money by hiring to the Dutch at a stiver a mile. They are much employed as riding is prescribed by the Dutch doctor as a corrector and preventative against diseases as befall people that have been long confined on shipboard."

The Statistical Account of 1791 – 1799 gives us details about ponies for some districts only. In Sandsting and Aithsting the number of horses "exceeds 800". The writer goes on to say that the ponies are sold to Dunrossness, Orkney or dealers in Lerwick who sell them on to Leith, London, Hull and Holland. At this time crofters were getting from £1 to £3 for them.

The number given for Tingwall, Whitness and Weisdale is 600 to 700 (horses and mares) while Unst is credited with nearly 1000.

In Walls and Sandness the writer says "a great number of horses are reared" and are "sold in great numbers to Orkney each year. Orkneymen come with quantities of linen which find a ready market."

The Account for North Yell and Fetlar is interesting because there were no cross-bred bigger ponies at this stage "... they answer our purpose in every point better than a larger breed."

The Rev. John Mill, who was a minister in Dunrossness from 1740 until 1803, kept a diary, and although most of it concerns his parish duties he occasionally mentions his animals. He had "glebe" lands extending to thirteen acres arable of excellent quality and fourteen acres of meadow. One parishioner, who could remember him said, "He usually went through the parish mounted on a native pony, with Hector, his man, following."

In 1773 Mill speaks of: "A young horse (of mine) was missing for some months and no accounts could be got of him, till a man in this village, who had gone in quest of one that had strayed from him, and in seeking his own horse he providentially lighted on mine, and brought him home without his own horse – the greater the mercy that horses can hardly be got for money, being scarce and dear."

In the year 1778 he says: "Horses, cattle etc were dying fast through the country through scarcity and badness of the fodder. I suffered in the common calamity – two horse beasts and nine cattle ..."

Shortly after that Mill tells us: "A fine young horse of the Norway breed had perished in a marsh, had it not been discovered in the daytime and seasonably rescued and the mercy was more remarkable as none I had fitted my wife so well for riding."

He must have kept his ponies inside for the worst of the winter for one day "... the whole roof of my stable fell down suddenly upon seven of my horses. ... they were none the worse. ... all Shetland ponies ..."

In 1793 Mill bemoans the lack of roads: "One of the principal means of improvement to this country would be good roads, as, at present, no cart or carriage whatever can be used for the transport of goods on the soft surface. ... and in some places the peat moss is so deep as to be impassable on horseback."

In *An Historic Description of the Zetland Islands* Thomas Gifford adds some interesting snippets to our knowledge. Writing in 1733 he includes horses in his list of exports. At this time they were exported mainly to Orkney and Scotland.

In listing the old Country Acts as well as those before mentioned for cutting tails or riding another man's horse he adds two more: "That all horfes belonging either to ulfcalders or infcalders, oppreffing and overlaying the neighbourhood be inftantly removed, after due advertizement given to their owners, and at the kirk door, under the pain of being confifcat and efcheat to the king" and "That none bring nor teather their horfes within the dicks of kirktowns, under the pain of 40 fhillings Scots, for each time they do to without liberty afked and granted." For the cost of horse hire he quotes "one fhilling Scots, the mile, and fomething to the boy".

A letter from Capt. Thomas Preston to Mr Ames included at the end of the book gives the price of a horse as a guinea and an ox a little less.

1800s

The 1800s saw many more visitors to Shetland and I have picked a few extracts of interest.

In 1806 a surgeon, aboard a Greenland whaling ship, finding men scarce in Lerwick to hire as crew, went on to Baltasound where:

> I made several expeditions into the country mounted on ponies. An Islander preceded me to point out the way. At first I thought my brains must have been dashed out, but I soon recovered from this panic. In the most wretched and precipitous paths, the animals never made a single false step, and travelled with considerable agility.

George Laurenson tenanted a farm at South Clickimin and from there he ran a horse hire business. We only know this because of his refusal, in August 1820, to hire horses to a group of gentlemen, and so he became the subject of a Petition to the Sheriff by James Greig. Part of the Petition states "... they required ponies ... fit to be rode". It does not state why George Laurenson withheld his horses, nor is there any record of the outcome of the Petition but we do know that one of the gentlemen in the party was Robert Stevenson, Engineer of the Scottish Lighthouse Commissioners, who was responsible for the construction of the Flugga lighthouse. Robert was grandfather of R. L. Stevenson.

It did not put George out of business at any rate for his son Robie succeeded him as horse hirer. In 1855 William R. Duncan states: "If a riding horse is wanted Robie o'Clickamin had a stud of Shelties at command". After Robie's death in 1872 his son, William, carried on the business.

Later on Ganson Brothers provided a horse and carriage hiring service in Lerwick.

David Brewster, L. L. D. in the *Edinburgh Encyclopaedia* of 1826 says:

> With respect to horses, Scotland possesses many distinct breeds and of remarkable qualities ... There are four distinct breeds of horses in Scotland, besides numerous varieties from each.
>
> The Shetland is probably among the most original, and is well known. Neglected as it is, it is a strong and hardy race, as well as docile and good-tempered. It never requires the house, and will undergo incessant work, without corn, while it will also carry weights equal to any horse of twice its stature. Of course it has comparatively little power in draught. Those who know only the rough animal, commonly exported at prices of twenty or thirty shillings, are scarcely aware of the beauty of this race under careful breeding often producing models on a small scale equal to the Arab.

Following his visit to Shetland in 1832, Edward Charleton, M.D. wrote, while staying at Belmont in Unst, "At an early hour the ladies went off to church upon their ponies each ornamented with it's peg and tether, done up in a neat knot upon it's shoulder". And a few days later, "We mounted two brisk little Shetland ponies and cantered away over the hills to Clugan and Muness Castle on the South East coast of the Island."

1835 – a quote from Robert Dunn (one of these self-styled "Naturalists" who shot everything in sight and made a great deal of money from selling the skins of birds to taxidermists and collectors):

> The usual charge in Shetland for horse-hire is about three pence per mile or you may engage for the day when you pay, according to the part of the

country you may be in from one shilling and sixpence to three shillings per day. The allowance to the guide is from 1/6d to 2/- per day; they will not scruple to ask more, and I should advise the traveller on all occasions to make a bargain before starting ...

There is one small house at Catfirth where I remained during the time the landlord was procuring the necessary number of men and horses to convey us to Osnafirth (Olnafirth). One of the horses which had been selected for his strength, carried 140 pounds of shot, on the other I placed my son and a little luggage; my guns and the remainder of the luggage were carried by the guides and women.

In 1839 L. A. Necker, a geologist, who travelled from Lerwick to Quendale by pony describes the rough terrain and goes on:

It is necessary to walk round the larger and deeper of the trenches and to jump over the others; the ponies acquit themselves marvellously in these two feats of dexterity. It is interesting to see them chose their route so sagaciously so as not to get caught in the quagmire, and to jump so nimbly, with the rider on their back, from one edge to the other of the numerous peat hags ... they are admirable animals, and cost nothing to feed. On arrival at a house the pony is released, after removal of the bridle and saddle, into a great walled pasture called a park, and there it is left to run and frolic at it's ease with numerous pony comrades ... I have seen in the space of twenty minutes or half an hour, cavalcades of twenty or thirty ponies, mounted by men, women and children, going to the peats.

1841 – a quote from Lauder and Wilson on a fact finding tour for the Board of Fisheries. They went angling at the Loch of Strand.

It was raining in torrents and some portions of what was called the road bore in our eyes a wild precarious aspect. But the Shetland ponies are proverbially sure footed, and they know their way ...

In 1842 the Artist Wm. Collins (who did illustrations for the *The Pirate*) travelled to Sumburgh with his son who writes:

The journey to Sumburgh Head, and back to Lerwick, occupied with deviations from the direct route, two days, including upwards of seventy miles of riding, and was performed on two shaggy little Shetland ponies, and on which the painter and his companion were at first positively ashamed to mount. The first day's journey – thirty miles – these wonderful little animals performed with ease, over a country which would have knocked up the strongest 'road hack' that ever was bred. At the latter part of the day, a dense dark mist coming on, in the middle of a solitary moor, their bridles were thrown over their necks, by order of the guide, who had lost his way, and who cooly observed that the ponies would find it, and moreover avoid the dangerous peat bogs, which intersected the peat moor in every direction. Thus left to their own guidance the sturdy little Shetlanders trotted along through drizzling rain and impenetrable mist, with their noses to the ground, like hounds on the scent, crossing each narrow tract of marsh, by jumping from one morsel of firm earth to another; never making a false step or showing a moments hesitation, or fatigue, for upwards of an hour, and stopped demurely, just as the vapour began to lift, opposite a gate and enclosure. Through these the guide led the way, and brought his travellers to a halt, opposite the parlour windows of a private house.

1845 – When a Free Church Minister was describing Lerwick he spoke of fishermen from Spain, Holland and France congregating about the quays and a group of Shelties for sale. He went on "This morning at six o'clock we got mounted, on two small but excellent ponies ... For the greater part of the journey to the south of the mainland there is not a track, ... but indeed most all parts of the mainland are accessible by means of these ponies."

This same minister on his way from Uyeasound to Baltasound "saw numbers of the finest ponies we had yet observed straying along the moor."

CHAPTER THREE

THE VERSATILE PONY

In Shetland's economy of subsistence nothing was wasted and the imaginative person could find a use for most materials. Peat was the crofters' only fuel; it was free and available in practically every district, but it was labour intensive. In many

The Irvine lady from Gulberwick had fled into the house because she wasn't "properly dressed" to have her photo taken.   © *Aberdeen University Library, G. W. Wilson Collection*

districts the peat "banks" were some distance from the crofts and here the ponies came into their own, carrying home the peats, pannier style. This whole process has been well described in previous publications. The last "peat flitting" was done in Unst in the early sixties.

Now there are tractors and with more money in the economy, a choice of fuels. It is interesting to note that the areas like Unst and Fetlar which required ponies for peat flitting kept more of them than, say, Yell where the crofters could have a peat bank practically at their door.

Besides the taking home of peat and the use of ponies for riding, which we shall consider later, they were used to many other advantages.

They were used for carrying muck from the byre in spring in small carts. As

Flitting peats in Unst, c.1900.   © *Shetland Museum*

Flitting peats by cart at Gloup, Yell, c.1930.   © *Shetland Museum*

14

soon as the cows could be put out to graze the layers of muck which had gathered during the winter had to be forked out. Sometimes there was such a build up of muck and straw or turves under the cows that a second wooden catch (vegwel) had to be placed in the wall at a higher level for tying up the cow. The muck kept dry in this way would be of better quality than that put outside.

Ponies were also used for bringing seaweed, which was high in potash, from the seashore, where it had been piled up, to the fields (usually the potato field).

Ploughing was occasionally done by the Shetland pony but could not have been terribly successful for on small crofts groups of people would get together and dig as a team making remarkable progress. On farms larger ponies were used.

For harrowing purposes they were used. The harrows were simply made by knocking long nails or hard wooden pegs into a wooden frame.

Either carts or "maeshies" could hold a big bulk of hay or corn when it came to harvest time. Small carts came in handy too for bringing up the potatoes or turnips to the barn.

One of the most unusual deployments I've heard of was when gentlemen were out shooting swans they used the ponies as a screen.

In Shetland long ago there was a rough fiddle called a "gue" or "gu". This was played by a bow using horse hair. The horse hair is taken from the horse's tail. Beneath a microscope the hair can be seen to be saw toothed and this is why vibrations occur when the bow is drawn across the strings. I don't suppose there

A pony took some of the drudgery out of shopping, c.1890.
© Aberdeen University Library, G. W. Wilson Collection

was much permabuca wood which only comes from South Africa to make the bow. It apparently is the only wood with the right amount of flexibility.

Horse hair was in great demand for fishing lines. I remember seeing my father make a line for a rod for catching "sillocks". He used peat ash on his fingers so that he could get enough tension for the twisting and twining. He liked a "toam" made like this because it gave a good spring.

Horse hair had to be removed very carefully so as not to remove the ponies precious protection. Laws were passed in 1612 to prevent the cruelty of docking tails at random.

In the early days of the Unst Agricultural Society last century a prize was awarded for a pair of gloves made from pony hair. That of course would have been the fine body hair. There is no word of the results.

During the war an experiment was tried out in Shetland with the breeding of silver foxes. Their food included worn out Shetland ponies.

Horse hair was also used successfully for making bird snares.

Ponies were often used for shopping. Ordinary goods could be carried by the pony with "kishies" while a cart would be used for heavier goods. Meal and flour, for instance, were often bought in 140lb bags.

Probably one of the most bizarre burdens a Shetland pony has ever carried is a World War II mine. This particular one was stranded at Sandwick in Unst. Having been diffused and its contents removed, Tom Stickle and Rudi Saunders decided to take it up to the croft at Hannigarth. Rudi says "... it took us a whole day, but we did it. There was great plans for what to do with the mine, but none of these ever came to fruition. All that happened was that Bella used it for keeping firewood and occasionally, if the bantam cock paid too much attention to the hens, he was imprisoned in it."

Rudi Saunders with World War II mine.

CHAPTER FOUR

EARLY EXPORTS

The ponies were part of everyday life in the islands and most crofts kept as many as they could afford, to carry home their peats or carry people, besides various chores round the croft which are considered in Chapter Three.

Some of the first recorded exports of ponies from Shetland went to Germany. In the Middle Ages there began a flourishing trade between Shetland and Germany, especially the ports of Bremen and Hamburg. As early as 1186 dried salted fish was being exported from Shetland to European countries through Bergen. The power of the Hanseatic League was growing, probably reaching its peak around 1400.

By the early 1500s German merchants were trading directly with Shetland. There are, for instance, at Lund in Unst, two huge slab tombstones to German merchants. It is impossible to decipher them now, but they have been well documented. One reads: "Here lies the worthy Segebad Detken, burgess and merchant of Bremen. He carried on his business in this country for 52 years, and fell blissfully asleep in our Lord in the year 1573 on the 20th of August, God rest his soul."

These traders in early summer brought with them a wide range of fishing gear, salt, alcohol, food, tobacco and clothes. In return, at the end of the fishing season, they carried back to Germany, fish (salted and dried), hides of various animals, knitted goods, a rough woollen cloth, fish oil for lamps, butter, mutton and ponies. At that stage only a few ponies were being exported.

A trickle of ponies also found their way to Holland over the years. By 1500 the Dutch were well aware of the vast shoals of herring around Shetland. To make best use of their fishing fleet the Dutch developed vessels, known as "buses", large enough to salt the fleets' catches of herring aboard and store them until their load was complete. The herring fishing was such a lucrative trade that it developed fast. Within a few years the herring fishing season was starting regularly on the 24th of June (Johnsmas) and so it remained for the next three centuries.

The favourite landing place for the Dutch was Bressay Sound, known to them as Bus Haven. So Lerwick developed due to the many contacts with the Dutch fishermen.

The doctors who travelled annually with the fleet recommended that the fishermen take exercise to counteract being cooped up in the confines of a fishing boat. This they did, and their favourite form of exercise became riding the Shetland ponies that gathered with their owners near the Lerwick shore. If various descriptions of the performances are to be believed we are tempted to conclude that the entertainment value was enjoyed even more than the riding itself.

In the *Zetland Times* of 17th June, 1872 there is a description of such an event:
> During their sojourn in Lerwick one day has been set apart from time immemorial for a very favourite passtime with the Dutchmen viz exercise on

horseback. Most amusing scenes are to be witnessed between the Hillhead and the Knab on this, Dutchmen's riding day. On that day dozens of those who have horses assemble, steeds in hand on a piece of ground above the town and thither to betake themselves, the horsey portion of the Dutch for twopence worth of equestrianism which consists of a gallop out for half a mile or so and back again.

For the most part women and boys are in charge of the steeds with every conceivable kind of halter from the decent saddle to the old and apparently rotten rope, some with saddles and stirrups, some with saddles without stirrups, some with a piece of coarse cloth or straw mat.

Here a great tall fellow goes up to a very little pony, pays his two pence – it is always prepaid – and prepares to mount. But how is he to get the sabot, with the point like the prow of his own bus, into the stirrups. It evidently can't be done. Off go the sabots, a shake is all that is necessary – and he gets into the saddle. At first he grasps only the bridle, but as the pace quickens, and it soon does that, for he means to have his twopence worth – you see his hand slips around to the back part of the saddle and take a firm hold. This is all very well but the saddle itself is shaky and the pony's back short so he must have more leverage by grasping the tail. There, he's all right but the motion is neither graceful nor easy and his hat flies off. This was expected so the woman or boy in charge follows behind."

So it goes on.

The "moor behind the town'" where the ponies were hired out was the stretch of ground from Annsbrae down to Braivik around the Sletts. To this day there is a cliff out at the Knab known as the Dutchman's Leap where, in the dim distance of time, one of these fishermen rode his pony over the edge with fatal results.

Needless to say some of the Hollanders saw the potential of these ponies as children's mounts and so at the end of the herring season in September it would not have been uncommon for a few Shetland ponies to cross the North Sea in the holds of these fishing boats. The children would have been delighted and the crofter who had sold the pony for £1 would also have been satisfied.

Up until the middle of the 18th century many ponies were exported from Shetland to Orkney. Sometimes they were bought for a pound or two but more often they were bartered for Orkney cloth – probably linen. I could find no record of when this trade began but for some reason after the mid 18th century it dwindled and the Orkney men obtained their ponies from Caithness, Strathnaver and Ross-Shire; perhaps the animals were simply larger and more able to cope with the heavy workload of an Orkney farm.

By 1770 a number of ponies were also finding their way to England. The Greenland whaling ships that called each year at Shetland to complete their crews would naturally call back along on their return from the Arctic when the season was over. A direct trip to Scottish and English ports plus the bonus of a few extra pounds for the enterprising skipper would have encouraged this trade in ponies.

All the exports combined would not have been great enough to upset the natural balance of the Shetland pony world whereas the demand from the pits certainly would and did.

CHAPTER FIVE

THE PIT TRADE

The passing of the Mines Act in 1842 had a huge impact on the Shetland pony. Ponies had been used before that in the mines but only on certain seams. It was only when women and children were no longer allowed to go down the mines that the floodgates opened as mine owners realised that small ponies could do the job of dragging bogies of coal along the tracks more efficiently.

It has been estimated that, at that particular date the number of ponies in Shetland numbered ten thousand. At that point there were comparatively few sheep but it is not possible to give an accurate figure.

A decision had been made to use only horses in the mines to avoid any fighting. The demand then was for males from four to twelve years, and, if possible, below forty inches at the withers.

Alexander Sandison had arrived in Uyeasound in the 1850s to work in his uncle's shop there. He kept accurate records of all aspects of the business, including the growing pony trade, and fortunately the majority of all letters received and copies of all letters sent have survived. I have separated these into 1) the pit trade which mostly involves dealers, 2) individual inquiries and stud matters 3) sarcoptic mange 4) special requests 5) the later American trade 6) The Shetland Pony Stud Book Society. As far as possible I have quoted letters verbatim.

By 1862 Alexander Sandison was building up his stud with some ponies in "halvers" with others. The person who owned the mare would "give" it to another person to look after on the understanding that any proceeds from a foal would be split in half or that the owner would have first offer of offspring. Alternatively sometimes a crofter would "sell" half his mare if he was short of money.

From Alexander Sandison's notebook:

State of Horse Stock in January 1862

(Rül = 1 year old)

2	A mare and foal in halvers with Wm Henry, Lumbister.
2	A mare and horse Rül in West a Firth, the mare my own the rül in halvers with C. Scollay.
5	3 mares, 1 mare rül pybald and 1 foal in halvers with J. Spence.
3	One horse and I mare and foal in halvers with Thomas Bain.
1	One old mare in halvers with the Kellister people.
2	Two grey mares in halvers with Allie.
1	Brown mare "Mary".
1	Brown horse "Garibaldi".
1	Brown mare "Fraser".
1	Pybald rül "Beauty".
1	Old black mare "Jane".
1	Her rül not yet found but hope she is not gone for good and all.

21.

Horse Stock Continued

1   One horse in halvers with Nicolas Moar, Cullivoe.
1   One mare in Vollaster the one half belongs to A. Anderson's daughter the other twixt Marjory, Tommy and Charlie.

May 10th Bought a little one year old horse from Andrew Cluness for 40/-
May 27th Bought a 4 year old mare from William Cluness, Sandwick, little but bonny for 70/-
Gave the old mare "Jane" and a foal to Charles Williamson, Westafirth, the two to be in halvers including the foal.

Note of Horse Stock Sold

1860   sold "Burton" in 1860 for £5.10
1861   sold "Napoleon" in 1861 for £5
1862   sold one little horse in halvers with Willm. Henry for £4.16
1862   sold "Bessy" to Mr Burchell for £6
       The half of the above mare belongs to Thomas Spence, Bixter, (paid him)
1862   Sold the little year old I bought from Andrew Cluness to Mr Burchell for £3.10/-
1862   Sold the 2 year old Horse I got from Westafirth to Mr A. Smith £5
1862   Sold my ox "Jack" to Mr Mill for £15.2.6
1863   The horse I had in halvers with Nicolas Moar my half for £3.5/- do. With Thos Bain, sold both to A. Jamieson £3.5/-
1864   Nov. Sold "Garibaldi" to Robert Mouat, Lund £6 –
1865   June Sold "Fernanda" to do. £7 –

Memorm. 1862

June – gave Charlotte Scollay the young mare I bought from William Cluness and took over here in place of the mare the horse rül, which I had halvers with her, the one to stand for the other.

This somewhat motley collection of ponies was the beginning of an important stud that in the 1890s could advertise in the *Livestock Journal*:

SANDISON, ALEXANDER, UYASOUND, SHETLAND, SCOTLAND. Pure-bred Shetland Ponies. Mr. Sandison has been a large breeder of Shetland Ponies for over thirty years. Upwards of 200 ponies may be seen on his farm, amongst which are some very fine specimens.

13th September, 1866. From John Anderson, Hillswick to Alexander Sandison:
Dear Sir,
    I enclose herewith cheque for £19.16/-, the amount of your account agreed by my servant Charles Charleson. I beg to thank you for your kindness in being obliging to him and me.
    This is the first year I have tried the Horse dealing – and I had no idea that he would get as many or I should have sent more cash with him.

June 1868. From Romyn & Co, Corn Merchants, Stocton-on-Tees. To Alexander Sandison:

Sir,

We have a good demand for Horse ponies 9 to 9½ hands high for mining purposes. Their value would be for £7 to £9 according to condition and age of the animal and about 20 to 25 would sell well.

Waiting your consignment,

19th October, 1870. From W. Hunton & Co formerly Romyn & Co, Stocton-on-Tees:

... a few good useful ponies from 9 to 11 hands would sell well here just now and shall be glad of your consignments. There was a sale of Spanish Ponies here last week and some sold for £26 each.

October 1872. From Spence & Co, Baltasound to Alexander Sandison:

... Mr McKenzie of Lawson & Son left an order here for 2, 2 year old mares, 1 stallion 2 year old, and a Horse any age under 4 years. Also 2, 2 year old Shetland Oxen ...

Yours truly,
J. Thomson

November 1873. From John Anderson, Hillswick:

... I enclose stamps 8/9, your charge for shipping 21 ponies on May 15th.

October 1874. From W.S. Smith, Lerwick to Alexander Sandison:

... ship them by return of boat marked B near sides as I may not get to mark them when they come here to be shipped from one boat to the other.

October 1874. From W.S. Smith to Alexander Sandison:

... The price I asked was £8.10/- a head and it's a question if I even get that, the former fancy prices are all done. You as well as others will have to be contented with less money.

1st July, 1874. From Alexander Sandison to John Walker (Garth):

Dear Sir,

Your letter to hand. I have today sent to N. Garth – the three Iceland ponies and also 2 young Shetland ones from Uyea.

I am, etc.

1874. From Alexander (Lewie) Sandison (eldest son of Alexander Sandison, born 1856. He became a minister) to Alexander Sandison:

Mr Robb (salesman) was in today ... He wanted for one of his firm a pair of good Shetland ponies. We called a muster and he got his "pick". Mouatt's young horse took his fancy very much only it was quite out of his line since he wanted what could drive at once ... my prize one and Andrew Fraser's ... good mares, perhaps in foal, a pair and at the best age would be £18.00. They are not an exact match so is to try Anderson.

We sold an Englishman this morning one of the two year old ones – John Coutts' one – for £8 but we have to pay the freight to Lerwick.

1874. Snippets from a notebook:

21st Sept	Sold to Mr Meiklejohn 2 horses for £26.10/-
8th Oct	Shipped to Meiklejohn 1 horse from Spence, Murrister – £16 (4 yrs)
10th Oct	Meiklejohn by cash for two mares and geese – £15
26th Nov	1 Mare bought from Robt. Spence, Murrister, 3yr old £6.10/-
27th Nov	1 yr old mare bought from Jas. Sinclair, South House £5.10/-
5th Dec	Sold my half of one year mare with Clark sisters and got pay from Mary – £2.11/-. Paid her 5/- for foddering them. Put corn to Mill.

1874. Notebook:

Horse bought Jan.	1 from Scott Abernethy – £5
	1 from Mgt. Robertson –£5
	1 from Miss Ingram – £6
	1 from Cath. Manson – £5
	3 from Mr Henderson
	1 from Arch. Smith
	1 horse from J. Williamson – £5
	1 from Daniel Fraser – £5

1 horse rül from Robert Spence to be delivered when he wishes – he not to get less than £7 but the highest currency if more given.
The animal is good – £8.

1874. Notebook:

Feb	1 Horse rül from Mags. Nisbet £7
	1 x 3 yr old. 1 x 2 yr old and 1 x 1 yr old from Mrs Edmonston
£23.	

Alexander Sandison was buying from all the north isles at this stage:

Feb	from Yell 10
April	4 horse rüls at £7.10/-
May	Horse rüls £8.
	Charleson around buying for J. Anderson, Hillswick.
June	15 ponies from Fetlar £127.10/-
	ponies from Whalsay £48
TOTAL	to date for year 1875 – 86.

Oct	1 x 2 yr old Horse from I.D. Moar	£11.11/-
Sept	Horses and mares bought	
	2 mares from W and T Isbister	£16
	1 from M. Spence	£9
	1 from Tony Anderson	£7.10/-

1874 ponies bought in Fetlar:

	2 Horses (Arthurson)	£16
	2 Horses - Hart, Smithfield	£14
	1 Horse. John Coutts	£8

1 x 2 yr old Mgt. Murray (Houll)	£11.11/-
1 x 4 yr old A. Henderson (Aith)	£12
1 horse John Hunter	£7.15/-
1 horse John A. Laurenson	£8

The following letters from Wm. Stevenson Smith, formerly W. & A. Smith, Lerwick show how keen the dealers were to buy.

23rd January, 1875, to Alexander Sandison:

Dear Sir,

I have got my instructions to buy all the horse ponies you can get. You will set to work at once and try and secure every good pony you can buy in Unst and Fetlar and North Yell ... The work would need to be speedily gone about or we are sure to get opposition. You will buy only good ones that can stand shipping at once ...

30th January, 1875:

Dear Sir,

I am just in receipt of your message, I am anxious to buy Mr Mouat's ponies if they are real good but I do expect them cheaper than last season. You better buy and arrange with him to get him to keep as long as possible and buy as low as possible. I heard today that Mr Meiklejohn went North to buy and if so is likely to give you plenty of opposition.

Yours truly,

Wm. S. Smith.

P.S. Mr Mouat should get a little more than others but £9 is more by far than I would get and I do not care to lose money for the sake of increasing numbers.

12th April, 1875:

... I have passed the Whalsay ponies through your account in my books ...

5th May, 1875:

... How many horses will Charleson have got? I hope he has not got many. I am paving the way for his return to the mainland. He wont get many there. How many ponies have you bought? I was calculating, 60 to 70. There is a good many of those shipped early in the season died in the south, which I am sorry for. They say they were too lean in condition ...

17th May, 1875:

... I suppose and hope you will manage to keep (the ponies) till the steamer comes back – indeed I would not care to take these young ones by the packets as they are so long coming and the ponies are apt to get lockjaw ...

Because of the high value of the ponies the shipping problems and care during their transport appeared to get sorted out quickly.

1st July, 1875 (regarding ponies being shipped to Lerwick from Yell):
> ... drive them to Burravoe and ship them on the steamer's return from Yell sound. I will send money by "Chieftain's Bride".

19th September, 1875:
> ... I will only ship one more waggon load this season.

J.M. Adie and Sons of Voe were also dealing in ponies at this point.
30th July, 1879:
> ... 13 ponies sent to J.M. Adie & Sons.

1878 – From Alexander Stephen, 19 Lodge Walk, Aberdeen to Alexander Sandison:
> ... along with 8 ponies for which I enclose check for £21. Ponies in no demand here.

This last statement we can take with a pinch of salt.

14th June, 1878. From Alexander Stephen to Alexander Sandison:
> ... Could you buy 6 or 8 very good old mares with good mouths of teeth and in fair condition, if they are dear I can't do with them. I could do with a few at a few shillings each like last year ... mark X on shoulder.

John Meiklejohn was a regular buyer.

12th February, 1876. From John Meiklejohn, Maryfield House, Bressay to Alexander Sandison:
> My Dear Sir,
> Would you kindly let me know what you are doing in horse foals and at what prices they are going, also say if you could secure 10 good ones for me at £8 or rather if I came North do you think I could get this number by your assistance.

8th February, 1879. From John Meiklejohn, Maryfield House, Bressay to Alexander Sandison:
> ... I am quite unable to say how you could buy (yearlings) and be safe taking delivery just now. You would require to get them at £3 each and even at that, unless trade improves, they would not pay,
> With kindest regards ...

22nd March, 1879. From John Meiklejohn to Alexander Sandison:
> ... our folks instructed me to buy no more as they are buying excellent ponies in England at the same price for work ... Could you kindly find out what you could buy Lady Nicolson's 3 year old mares and horses at? I have got a faint hope of a private offer for such and I would buy thro. you if you pleased as your enquiries would not tend to put up Colin's idea of value so much ...

People saw £ signs when Meiklejohn appeared.

29th March, 1879. From John Meiklejohn:
As to Colin (Arthurson – factor for Lady Nicolson) – it is an order we are expecting – so I cannot quote any price only please try Colin for his really lowest selling price and if we get the order we will run shares with you or pay you commission if you prefer.

10th May, 1879. From John Meiklejohn:
... Since you cannot supply the (4) mares I have another offer to make you. A friend is buying some 2 year old horse ponies and I could get him to take a lot from you if you could deliver them free at Lerwick at £7 each ...

1879. From Miss Mouat, Gardie House to Alexander Sandison:
... I have by the same post a letter from J. Jaffrey (Belmont) asking if I wish to sell my horse ponies in Linga ... They are really beauties – but I must trust your saying a price. The ponies are a little more than 1½ years old.

1880. From Thos. M. Adie & Sons, General Merchants, Fish Curers, Voe to Alexander Sandison (Haggling over a quote for horses):
... and if we can see our way to come within a pound of your price we shall hope to do business ...

Many of these ponies destined for the mines were passing through the hands of three dealers who each took their cut.

16th June, 1881. From Wm. Manson, Weisdale:
... I received your favour and here enclose cheque £200.00 – could you not manage to keep the ponies on till July. I am so overstocked at present ... Then I will have some cleared off.

15th August, 1881. From Wm Manson, Weisdale:
... I here enclose cheque for £200. I hope you will excuse delay. Ship ponies to be landed at Vidlin ... and please mark I on their rump. I hope they are all small sizes. Could you supply me with 2, 2 yr old mares biggish size and good shapes and condition at £5 each. (also 2 fat heifers at £5 each).

1881. From Anderson Manson (dealing in ponies, cattle and sheep) to Alexander Sandison.
1st April:
... send your 5 ponies by the first turn of Steamer and ship them to Vidlin ... bad accounts from England (regarding the state of the pony trade).

15th April:
... 5 ponies received and I enclose a cheque for £48 for price of the same ... one can't rise itself – very likely you or your son John is not been at the picking of it ... please write and let me know the least price you will take for

10 good conditioned ponies – horses I mean and also mention what for a few mares 2 and 3 years old.

P.S. the fine weather is come at last and things will get on much better now. There is not much doing at the fishing.

A. M.

(They were both heavily involved in the fishing industry).

1882. From R. I. Shafto, Durham to Alexander Sandison:

3rd March,

Have you any Shetland ponies with some Horse teeth from 9 - 10 hands high and what price do you want for them ? Is there any pony disease in your country ?

24th March,

... what price for 20 or 30 Shetland Horse ponies now two years old, thick, strong, sound and healthy and in good condition ... no higher than 10 hands and one inch ... Can you keep them to 1st May.

14th April,

... if you can keep the ponies till the 1st July I will send a person to see them ... It would be folly to bring the ponies out of the Islands in their present condition.

March 1881. From Alexander Stephen, 19 Lodge Walk, Aberdeen:

... 9 ponies for which I enclose £49.10/- ... What could you supply me with 2 yr old horses, small size and good condition ... Have you any coloured ponies black and white ?

1883. From Samuel Christie, Braehead Farm, Stirling:

January,

... 12 horse and 8 mares ... horses all 2 years old come Belting ... colours, brown and black of the "peerie" breed.

21st August,

... I will give you £37 for the lot (6 mares) shipped at Lerwick.

12th September,

... took delivery of the ponies and I was well pleased with them – sold 4 today

... I will give you £26 for four mares – black from 3 to 7 years, 40-43 inches

... expectation of order for 15 horse ponies 2 to 7 years old.

The buoyant trade continued. Alex Stephen, one of the biggest dealers came to the North Isles at the end of January – brave man.

February 1882. From Alex Stephen:

... looking for 30 horse ponies of small size all black and brown ... also 10 – 12 horse foals ...

A selection of Alex Stephen's letter headings is of interest as the trade develops. I particularly like the "communication in any language" considering the problems he had in English. Some years he wrote over thirty letters to Alexander Sandison, short and to the point. He concentrated on the cheaper end of the market but was always on the lookout for something unusual, as the following extracts show:

Lemon Place, Aberdeen,....................... 190 5

ALEX. STEPHEN, BREEDER AND EXPORTER OF ... SHETLAND AND HIGHLAND PONIES.

1882. From Alex Stephen:
5th May,
   ... what height is your smallest 2 year old ?

3rd July,
   ... one bull and two cows of the very smallest you can find ... also one ram and two ewes of the smallest breed of sheep.

24th July,
   ... more small animals ...

Alex. Stephen, Coach Builder, Dealer in Harness, Horses, Cobs, and Shetland, Welsh, and Highland Ponies.

9th August,
... could you send one of Lady Nicolson's entire ponies – I mean a Buty.

1882 – In this year alone Alexander Sandison shipped approximately ninety ponies to Alex Stephen. This leads me to believe previous estimates of ponies leaving Shetland are far too low. George Stephen was also a dealer, but he was more selective and prepared to pay for what he wanted. It is not known if he was related to Alex Stephen.

From George Stephen ... looking for more pairs:
March/April 1882,
... He won't have them unless they are a dead match ...

1883:
... have you got a handsome black mare pony, black or brown, 2 years old in fine fat condition ... send the two blue ponies ... I will be obliged if you will put a few sheafs of fodder on board with them ...

8th June, 1882 – George Stephen encloses a cutting of the launching of the *St. Rognvald* at Aberdeen, bringing the number of vessels belonging to North of Scotland Shipping Company to five. One was a paddle steamer engaged in Clyde trade. (On the back of the article is an advert for Assisted Emigration to Canada, £3 for Agriculturalists, £4 for others.)

February 1883. From H. J. Ritter, Lerwick (this dealer was stuck in Lerwick with bad weather):
> ... £45 for the balance due you.
> I wired you this morning offering you £7 and £8 for mares of my kind ... I hardly know when I will be able to leave Shetland as this weather has changed my plans altogether. Since I must stay I might as well take all the ponies that I can find that will suit me.

A great deal of business was done by wire at this stage.

July 1883. From Samuel Christie, Stirling:
> ... As our great Falkirk markets are now about to take place. I could now do with a lot of Shetland ponies (20, various kinds).

1883. From Alex Stephen:
> ... I find the steamer to call at Uyasound next week so kindly pick 10 – 12 good small pony mares rising three years at your price in your telegraph £7 and send them all as near matched pairs as you can, long tails and manes in good condition also cheap old mare or two and 8 young mares in foal ...

March,
> ... at what price 20 small hors ponies rising 2 yr ?

April,
> ... I am just got out of Yell after seeing the blunder that man has made with the ponies. I was especially to have been getting 2 yr old not 1 yr old horses, if you have any 1 yr old mares I will give you £5 each for them ...

May,
> ... enclosed find cheque valued £506 with thanks for your kindness.

October,
> ... your lowest price for 20 – 30 horses rising 3 yr old.

1884. From Alex Stephen:
> ... still open to take one or two foals 30in high at £4.10/- also 1 or 2, 31in at £4 if red and white or black and white... and what price would you supply fish livers per 100 weight and barrels to put them in? ... what is your price for 20 horse foals rising 2 years?

1885. From Anderson Manson, Laxfirth to Alexander Sandison:
March,
Dear Sir,
Sorry your account has been so long but I was unwilling to pay out cash to you that has plenty of it until I got it – especially when I had no profit on the transaction. I herewith enclose your cheque for £12 and Mr Meiklejohn's letter to show I have no profit on the transaction. Please say by return of post what ponies you have for sale ...

(nothing daunted he bargains for more)

April, to John P. Sandison, son of Alexander and father of Ian Sandison of Houlland:
... prices of horses and mares ? How many cheviot hoggs do you want at 25/- to over 30/-?

May,
... how many horses can you supply under £9 ?

August,
... £48 for last lot of ponies asked from your son Charles at Baltasound.

1886. From John Meiklejohn, Maryfield, Bressay to Alexander Sandison:
12th August,
... I will come North and see the ponies and cattle ...

10th September,
... Could you supply me with 2 year old mares with square mouths, one yearling horse, one yearling mare, one two year old horse and one two year old mare as small sizes as you can and if so at what cost ?
I would like these per "St Magnus" so would like to have quotations by wire on receipt of this and also say if you would send me on Wed per "Earl" two yearling mares, black or one black and one brown at about £4 each.
With kind regards,
Yours truly,

1884. From Jas. Duncan to Alexander Sandison:
July,
... (from a batch he bought earlier) ... I got the silver medal for my Entire which will look as well and last longer than a £1 note. You will see the prize list in the paper ...

August,
... cheque for £90 stg. In payment of 10 ponies sent me. I am mostly sold out now.

April 1885. From T. M. Adie, Voe to J. P. Sandison:
... 2 yr old ponies ... I could not buy them at your price just now but if you will keep them till the end of June I will take them at £9 each provided none are over 40 inches.

June 1885. From T. M. Adie, Voe to Alexander Sandison:
> ... only been able to sell 10 this season. They seem to be at a complete standstill all over. If you have not disposed of the two small 3 year olds I can take them at £28 for the pair if under 40 inches. I have nearly 40 2 year olds here just now ...

August 1885. From T. M. Adie, Voe to Alexander Sandison:
> ... 2 yr old ponies, please quote lowest price for 6 not exceeding 41in ... the white fish industry won't make us fat this season ...

1885. From John Anderson, Hillswick:

February,
> ... re. the 10 horse ponies rising three from 38" - 40" I will give £8 for each on 1st week of March. I am sorry to learn you have so many herrings unsold. The cholera in Spain I fear is telling on the sale of our fish. I am sorry to hear of scab in Fetlar, as I know too well what it is.

This will be dealt with in another chapter as it had such implications for the trade.

1886. From John Meiklejohn to Alexander Sandison:

June,
> ... require from one to ten mare ponies from 3 to 6 years old to be delivered here not later than Monday of nest week. I can do with any colour but they must be strong enough to stand a journey.

July,
> ... sorry you have no mares ... how much for your horses ?

1885. From Anderson Manson to Alexander Sandison:

April,
> ... trade is very stiff ...

July,
> ... I had bought from your son John 10 x 2 year old ponies 40 inches and under in fresh condition at £8.10/- to be lifted in two or three weeks.
>
> I will take your four three year old ponies delivered in Lerwick if not over 40 inches at £13 per head.

1885. From George Stephen, Aberdeen to Alexander Sandison:

March,
> ... I am glad one of the four is under 33".

14th May, (quibbling price)
> ... I know where I can get 10 to 14 on the mainland at £8 each.

19th May, (it worked)
> ... I am glad you accepted my offer for 20 ponies ...

26th May,
... 20 ponies arrived safe. Please find cheque for £160.

14th June, (after being in Unst)
... 20 more 2 yr old horses ...

July,
... the 3 matched pair were very good and handsome ponies, (re purchase of
2 little grey ponies he had seen beside Alexander Sandison) I did not intend
to give you more than £11 for the little things so you can send the wife a
couple of nice shoulders shawls.

1885. From John Spence, Haroldswick to John P. Sandsion (bargaining to sell
ponies at 5/- commission each):

3 one yr old horse ponies	@	£5.5/- each
2 one yr old mares	@	£5.10/-each
4 one yr old mares	@	£4.5/- each
1 one yr old mare	@	£4.10/- each
3 two yr old horse ponies	@	£8.5/- each
2 mares about 7 years old	@	£8. each
1 mare	@	£9.

John P. Sandison (son of Alexander) replied that he would take the young ones
but not the mares at that price.

February 1887. From Anderson Manson:
... you may say ponies is scarce but I'm afraid not. I could buy just now the
most of one hundred ponies rising three years which is a case I never saw
since I commenced the trade.

15th October, 1887. From Leonard Lyall, M.P.:
... sorry to hear of the losses suffered by the Fetlar crofters through the pony
disease. This rearing of good Shetland Ponies ought to be the most paying
branch of the crofter land industry. No animal reared on the islands is worth
so much when 2 or three years old as your pony.
I hope the Crofters Commission's visit here may not be very long delayed
and that the feeling of security and of fair play which should result from the
enquiry and the decisions about rent will cause the breeding of ponies to be
taken up again to the advantage of crofter and profit when sold.

February 1887. From Wm. Henderson, Burravoe, Yell to Alexander Sandison:
... the 3 year old horses and 2 year old horses are nice tidy little things (about
40 inches when last measured) I have given you a list of mares and I must
draw your attention to the four Horse foals (one year old in May). They are
small and neat.
I have always been particular as to the breeding of our ponies. I can assure
you that no cross of Scotch is in them to my knowledge but good feeding has
improved them.

I feel sure that Wm. Henderson's last statement is a profound one. The studs that could afford to feed their ponies had far better stock and those that couldn't were mostly responsible for the weak hocks found.

1885. From A. G. Kidston & Co. Glasgow:

... correspondents of ours in Canada wish to know the price at which we could get then some Shetland Ponies, a Stallion and several mares for breeding purposes. They are intended for use in mines in Canada ... price in Shetland and freight to Leith or Glasgow, average size and best time of year to ship them ?

1890. Following the formation of the Stud Book in 1890 prices moved up for a time hence the complaint from Thomas Atkinson, Coal Exporter, Newcastle:

6th February,

... If prices are rushed up for Shetland ponies then my buyers will go for the Polish ones which are cheaper if not so tractable. 10 of them arrived at Leith
...
I have orders for 50 or 60 more ... Please wire me.

11th February,

Your parcel of 10 was as nice a lot as I have seen for many years and if you will be advised don't let that breed slip from your hands. The crossing going on with inferior animals at present in Shetland will very soon ruin the trade if not checked.

From T. Atkinson to Alexander Sandison:

... Go beyond the £9 and in come the Russian ponies 3, 4, 5 and 6 years old at this price. They are 11 hands high.

Another attractive letter heading.

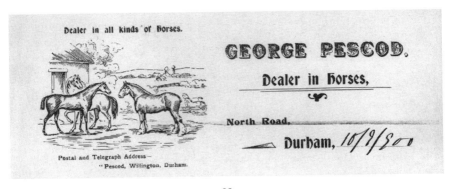

Dealer in all kinds of Horses.

GEORGE PESCOD.

Dealer in Horses,

North Road.

Durham, 10/9/80

Postal and Telegraph Address—
" Pescod, Willington, Durham.

From Alexander Sandison to Gavin Hadden (who was prepared to buy and pay for only the best):

January,

> ... we shall spare you two of our best three year old mares ...

February,

> ... Since I sold to you I have bought three ponies and have shipped two of them for you, keeping one, a Skewbald, as I think I may keep him for a stallion and put a few mares to him.
>
> I could gave got £20 each for four of those now shipped to you. There has been as many as four buyers in this Island at one time and they gave tempting prices but only got a few – there was only one three year old horse for sale, a big rough one, and they gave £16 for it ...

1ˢᵗ February, 1890. From Alexander Sandison to Mr Shand (Shipping Co.):

> ... I have shipped to you 24 ponies I wired you about by "Earl" today and I feel sure you will give orders to have them well looked after and properly fed and watered.

4ᵗʰ February, 1890. From Alexander Sandison to George Bruce, S.P.S.B.S.:

> ... except the few I still have unsold there is not a pony in this island (Unst) to be had at any price. I shipped 24 this week, 8 of them 3 year old stallions for Mr Hadden.
>
> I am very pleased to hear that "Tom Thumb" was sold for £50. Among those now shipped to Mr Hadden there are, I think 3 or 4 which will equal "Tom Thumb" when his age.

1890. From T. Atkinson, Newcastle to Alexander Sandison:

> ... Be sure to mark the ponies, advising me of the same as I am under the impression that I have not always got the ponies intended for me. Unless they are marked it is quite possible for dealers travelling by the same boat to make an exchange should it have advantage to them.

He was receiving 10 x 2 year old horses at £13.6/- (6/- freight to Lerwick).
1891. From Alexander Sandison to T. McKinnon Wood:

My Dear Tom,

> Seeing they would not allow us to have a "Sea Horse" trademark we have thought of trying a land horse. He might not look in his element among the ling, cod and herrings but he has got some go in him and looks as if he would take the eye and be remembered. Willie has drawn and sketched the pony and he thinks he will manage to make a good stencil for it.

1892. From Alexander Sandison to Thomas Atkinson:

> ... I may point out that you cannot get in Shetland ponies rising 2 years, older than those which I offered you. To my certain knowledge some Dealers make a practice of representing these ponies to be older than they really are. It is necessary for buyers to be on their guard in reference to this matter.

10th October, 1891. From Alexander Sandison to Gavin Hadden:
... you think £12 per pony for yearlings a startling price. What would you
think of £7 being freely given for foals 5 months old and shipped out now?

In a letter to Gavin Hadden in December 1891 Alexander Sandison lists 52
ponies for sale, mostly rising 2. Some with sire and dam, but colours and sizes
rather than names. Gavin Hadden bought 34 of them in January 1892.

Alex Stephen had been out of the running for a bit, due to high prices but in
1896 a letter from him:
... I will give you £3 for the pair. You see the last two I got one of them died
and other is lick a racehorse so send them on.

October 1897. To Gavin Hadden from Alexander Sandison & Sons:
For mares rising two years we expect £6, rising three £7.10/-, rising four £9
and rising five £10. The mares rising four and five years are in foal, and are
very fine ponies.
    We have also on hand two or three beautiful little stallions, worth looking
after if you require such.
    We have sold over seventy ponies this year, mostly horses. To Lady Hope
we sold two very fine little stallions in Spring ...

1897. From Thomas Atkinson to Alexander Sandison:
... Our market is simply inundated with Russian, Polish, Faroe, Welsh and
Shetland as our collieries are altering their mode of working their thin seams
so the cheaper Russian, Polish and Faroe animals are being preferred.
(£8 being paid for ponies rising three years.)

1897. From Anderson Manson to Alexander Sandison:
... The pony trade is quiet and some of the old pits are worked out and the
American trade done.

1897. From George Stephen to Alexander Sandison.
... I submitted your offer of the 20 ponies to my client but he says 3 year olds
are too young for the pits. They won't buy until they are four or five years.
He is coming here on Saturday to buy some from Messrs Smith the
Fishcurers – they have a good many and I hear during the winter they have
lost between 30 and 40.

1897. From Alex Stephen to Alexander Sandison:
... Will you tack £32 for the year olds? ... You will have to send Mrs Stephen
a Shetland shale for a luck penny.

10th October, 1898. From Brydon, Seaham Harbour to Alexander Sandison:
... I am sorry to tell you we had a very poor sale for Shetland ponies. Nearly
all our buyers were absent for one cause or another.
    Messrs Crow of Sunderland are the most likely people to sell your ponies

in this district, but after the trade we had last week I would be shy to recommend you to them in the meantime.

You would not easily get grass here for the Winter as the land is highly rented and the charge would be more than it is worth.

With kind regards,

April 1898. Letter to MacDonald, Fraser and Co. Ltd, Livestock Salesmen, Perth from Alexander Sandison:

... pleased to send a consignment (to special sale) but we would like to know before sending whether the ponies to be exposed for sale will be in rough or fed up and groomed. Ponies in the rough shaggy state from the winter pasture would make a poor show alongside well-fed and groomed ponies and would get but scant justice at the hands of the buyers.

1898. From Perth Auction Mart (MacDonald, Fraser and Co) to Alexander Sandison and Sons:

... We have arranged to hold a special sale of Shetland Ponies on Monday 8th May next and sincerely hope you will favour us with a consignment. As it is highly important that this sale should be advertised in all the leading papers at home and abroad, particularly in America we trust you will intimate your entries as soon as possible in order that we may advertise them without delay and so give buyers ample time to come from a long distance.

10th April, 1899:

... In regard to the 3 and 4 year old Horse ponies you have for sale you need have no hesitation in sending them here to the sale because if we are able to adverise such a lot of horse ponies we would get all the coal owners in Scotland and England to attend the sale as these are just the class they are in want of.

25th April, 1899. From Caledonian Railway Co., Aberdeen:

(re Ponies for Perth)

Quote from Aberdeen to Perth

Part truck or 4 ponies –

43/4 at Owner's risk.

4 Ponies – 79/10 at Company's risk.

1 or 2 ponies – 39/11 at Company's risk.

1897. From Anderson Manson, Maryfield, Bressay:

... will take 2, 3 year olds and 24, 1 year olds colour black, brown or bay. I will give you £7 for them at Lerwick.

This was quite a drop from the "£7 freely given for horse foals 5 months old", but still a good price.

16th July, 1900. From Anderson Manson to Messrs Sandison:

... on the death of Alexander Sandison of Uyasound ... I feel as I have to miss a friend by the death of your father.

1902. From Alex Stephen to A. Sandison and Sons:
... Can you offer me anything out of the Common run of things – what no
one else has, that is what I have customers for at all times.

1903. Alex Stephen wrote 30 letter to A. Sandison and Sons this year from his
new premises at Lemon Place, while George Stephen wrote 31.

August 1903. From Alex Stephen (his spelling did not improve):
... If you find the 2 horse foals 29 inches at £2.10/- each send them on in
good order. Pedgree no mater ... and if you come across a small foal with a
worthless old mar you could buy her for me £1.5/- to £1.10/- buy them for
me.
P.S. State Lowest price per ton for salt fish any kind and cheap and Rock
Dried i have a customer.

3rd December,
... I am sorry to state the trad in ponies is all to pices – no trad – 30 letters
from Rusa, Germany and France – all the talk is no money – no money o
these forners tha mack me sick.
Wishing you all a Mery Crismas and a Prospres New Year.

February 1903. From George Stephen. (re having pony skin dressed):
... I meant the pony stood me about £10, not the dressing of the skin. I would
think the one you sent will cost from 6/- to 10/- when it is finished which
takes a good while.

January 1903. From George Stephen. (re small foals):
... The Showman I expected about the Horse Ponies did not turn up. Some
of these chaps only want ponies from the 6d Bazaar, 12 for 18 pence and a
luck penny back.

Further disillusionment for George Stephen a week later following a complaint
from a customer:
... some of them think it is a £1,000 race horse they are writing about and
not a £10 pony.

March 1903. From George Stephen:
... The ponies arrived safe. The two mares are nice ponies – one of horses
fair – the other a duffer.

April 1903:
... When the pony walks or trots you see and hear the joint click, click and
they are very stiff and an eye sore, if not unsound.

May 1903:
... I would take the 5 ponies offered if they are good handsome ponies in
good condition at your price if you would allow me 10/- luck.

It is amazing how many dealers asked for and got, a "luck penny" in cash or kind.

May 1903:

... Ponies arrived safe, the Bays are right good ponies, the foal is a nice one but mare too big and bulky. It is not fair to charge 15/6 or more (freight) for a pony costing £6 or less.

July 1903:

... About the horses. I have not had an enquiry this year about pit ponies. The Newcastle men have got the hold and apparently they will keep it for pit ponies.

July 1903. From George Stephen (re mares for South Africa):

... the mares in foal I wired you about were for Marchioness Cunningham. I have sold her lots of ponies in the past but she has asked me a good many times since to quote for ponies and I think she gets them from someone else. I quoted keen this time so I will see how she shapes.

July 1903:

... Manson sold at Reith and Anderson's on Friday 25 and 30 fair ponies. The prices on most of them was low.

June 1904. From Anderson Manson, Maryfield, Bressay:

... unless you can deliver at Lerwick good strong boned ponies in fresh condition, 4 year old horse at £8.10/- I must buy them elsewhere ... trade is miserable, being in Newcastle last week I have seen for myself. Four year old ponies are selling there by auction from £7 to £9 and in fresh condition, but I am glad to say I wasn't the owner.
Yours faithfully,

1904. From John Anderson and Sons, Hillswick:

... we have been buying a good few four year old ponies on the mainland (Shetland) lately at from £6 each for small, up to £8 for large sized ones, and looking at the state of the trade at present we are not inclined to go in for your large lot just now ...

November 1905. From George Stephen:

... Ponies have been selling at Duncans very cheap. Peter Anderson from Lerwick sold about 40 some weeks ago – the foals – some very good ones averaged about £2.10/- and old mares from about 15/-.

These prices may have been poor in comparison to what had been previously but looked at under the Retail Price Index would not look so bad today.

The Mines Trade continued on a lesser scale for many years. Barnie Covitz was still buying pit ponies in the 1960s, and it was not until 1994 that the last pit ponies were retired.

Ponies in a sixareen, Uyeasound, c.1905.   © *Shetland Museum*

CHAPTER SIX

STUD BUSINESS & A ROYAL REQUEST

The first record I could find of Alexander Sandison's stud was the following in 1859:

> Mare "Jane" rising 15 years.
> Her colt (by Wm Jaffrey's Horse) was foaled 28th June 1858.
> Grey mare foaled 2nd week of June 1857.
> Her daughter foaled 19th May 1859.

November 1872. Letter from John Meiklejohn, South Delting to Alexander Sandison:

> My Dear Sir,
> I herewith send you an order on Mr Walker for the price of pony agreed yesterday by him. I think this price very large but when we meet I trust you will return me a handsome luck penny.
> With best respects for yourself, Mrs Sandison and family,
>> I am,
>>> Dear Sir,
>>>> Yours very truly,

1874:

> Prizes taken at Unst Agricultural Show.
> Entire pony over 3yrs – 2nd - 5/-
> Entire pony under 3yrs – 2nd - 5/-
> Brood mare – 1st - 5/-

11th May, 1875. From John Meiklejohn, Maryfield House, Bressay:

> Dear Sir,
> In accordance with your request, I send you per "Aspara" today two Shetland Stallions, you will find them strong and fit for their work.
> Enclosed I send a copy of the only conditions on which I can give out these ponies, a duplicate of which please stamp and return to me. Mrs Meiklejohn joins me in kind regards to Mrs Sandison and yourself.
>> I remain,
>>> Yours ever truly,
> P.S. The ponies are marked L on the near fore hoof.

Having this day received from the Most Noble the Marquis of Londonderry two Shetland pony Stallions for the use of my mares and the mares of other owners which I may see proper to serve with the above mentioned Stallions I hereby guarantee that all stock got by these Stallions shall at anytime they may be for sale be first offered on equal terms to the Owner (or agent for the owners) of the said Stallions above mentioned.

Further I guarantee to return these stallions in similar condition to that which I have received and I stand all risk to the amt. of their value as may be fixed by ponies of a similar age and breed in the event of death by accident or otherwise.

February 1876. From Meiklejohn to Alexander Sandison:
... horse foals ... If you could secure 10 good ones for me at £8.

Unfortunately we do not know which stallions were sent to Unst. I presume Alexander Sandison was not given the information or he would have entered the resulting progeny from them when the Stud Book opened.

1879. From Colin Arthurson (Estate manager for Lady Nicolson, Brough Lodge, Fetlar) to Alexander Sandison:
April,
> ... as to three year old mares we may sell a few ... they differ much in size ... the same with the horses, is all in good condition, both 2 and 3 years olds. (re. Old cream mare which died going South) ... I am sorry she was sold as her offspring was about the best on the estate.

May,
> ... The cream two year old mare is 42½ inches and her price in Fetlar is £8.8/-, she is as fat as a 'tistey' (guillimot).
> P.S. I am sorry to say we cannot find a matched pair of mares at the height you want.

There was obviously a difference of opinion about the management of the stock and when Sir Arthur Nicolson took over in 1891 he wrote:
> It is well known in Shetland the late Sir Arthur was noted for keeping well bred stock, his ponies especially were acknowledged to be the best in Shetland; now they are certainly the worst. This has been caused by breeding in and in, and by bad management generally. Lady Nicolson would not go to any expense whatever in keeping up the breed by getting new bloodstock for the mares.

The quality of Sir Arthur's stock was also well known outwith Shetland. Again and again Alexander Sandison is specially asked for the 12 to 14 hands Fetlar animals from a wide variety of locations in the U.K.

April 1879. From John Meiklejohn, Bressay to Alexander Sandison:
> ... I am very sorry for all the trouble I have caused you in the Fetlar pony matter. The gentlemen in Egham thinks they are much too dear ... glad to hear what condition Colin's ponies are in and how they have stood the winter. Ours have lived well but they have cost us a deal of feeding.
> With warmest regards,

1885. From James Duncan, Fern Villa, Inverness to J. P. Sandison:
> ... a friend of mine wants a matched pair of mare ponies, black, strong and very handsome for a phaeton – sound and 3 - 8 years old and 10 - 11 hands high.

December 1884. From Charles S. Arthur, Burrafirth School House to Alexander Sandison:
> As I am anxious to put something into my account with your shop at Skibhoul and my pension has not come to hand yet, I wish you to get the mare and foal I named to you. She is worth about £10 and the foal £3 however I shall not limit the price having proved you before.

THE ROYAL STAMP

The following letters are all concerned with the ponies that were bought by Queen Victoria:

3rd October, 1887. From Dr Alex Profeit to John Duncan (Cattle salesman to the Queen):
> ... the ponies must be castrated and I should like them if possible not too broad in the back as they are intended for the young Prince of Connaught to ride ...

October 1887. From Alexander Sandison to John Duncan:
> ... thank you very much for thinking of me when you got the order for ponies for Her Majesty the Queen.
>
> We have on hand 14, three year old Horse Ponies all very fine from 36 to 42 inches high. For some years now we have been breeding with great care and trying to keep all the ponies 40 inches and under. The great demand has been for small sized, round Barrelled, good strong boned, full chested and well made ponies.
>
> We shipped 20 Horse ponies to your neighbour Mr Hadden all under 36 inches, but very fine.
>
> We have a pair of very dark Brown, strong well made and handsome Horse ponies 40 inches and a pair of Blacks 42 inches.
>
> If we have a suitable pair would you wish us to castrate them, or would you do it South. The Spring of the year we consider the best time.
>
> You will kindly let us know what height would be preferred. The pair of browns are very fine.
>
> You speak of ponies up to 44 inches – that size we would not consider true old Shetlands.

From John Duncan to Alexander Sandison:
> ... thank you for your note which I received on Friday and forwarded to Mr Profeit ... and advised him to take the browns. It will be a short time before he can give an answer as he has to refer the matter to the Queen.

5th October, 1887. From John Duncan to Alexander Sandison:
> ... I sent your letter to Dr Profeit and now enclose his reply. If the dark brown pair are not too broad in the back I think it would be best to take them ... so that they may be at Balmoral before the Queen leaves.

14th October, 1887. Further:

... you can get the ponies castrated and send them when they are right. There is no hurry as they are not to be used till Spring and it is of little importance for the Queen to see them before that time.

From Alexander Sandison to J. Duncan:

... I would rather send them up entire and have them gelded in Aberdeen – at my risk and cost. The Queen (still at Balmoral) could see them on arrival and the operation be performed at a suitable time after.

31st October, 1887. From J. Duncan to Alexander Sandison:

... I enclose telegram I received today from Mr Profeit about the ponies. The Queen is staying longer than expected at Balmoral owing to the birth of a daughter to Princess Beatrice and will likely be about a month yet.

You would therefore oblige if you could get the ponies sent with safety as early as possible so that she might see them before she leaves. I am sorry to put you to so much trouble but it seems Her Majesty is anxious to see them before her departure.

Yours faithfully,

14th November, 1887. From J. Duncan to Alexander Sandison:

... The ponies came to hand all safe and I forwarded them to Balmoral last Wednesday ... I thought them a pair of very handsome ponies and am greatly obliged to you for all your trouble about them. I will write you with Friday's mail and let you know what Her Majesty thinks of them.

21st November, 1887. From J. Duncan to Alexander Sandison:

... I received your telegram about the ponies and I hope they will arrive safe and that they will please. Her Majesty would not have the two ponies without being gelded, and they had a Veterinary Surgeon out of Aberdeen to perform the operation but I said I could get the two which were gelded before and I would take the pair of entires and sell them. I am sorry to give you so much trouble but they are very bad to please.

28th November, 1887. From J. Duncan to Alexander Sandison:

... The ponies [the 2nd pair of black geldings] came to hand all right and I sent them to Balmoral last Wednesday ... I am not aware if they will keep all four.

1st December, 1887. From J. Duncan to Alexander Sandison:

... I understand that Her Majesty is well pleased with the last pair of ponies. She liked the first pair well enough but only objected to their being entire.

Meantime I enclose a cheque for £56 (payment for 4 ponies) and when I see the Commissioner if he thinks them worth more I will remit the difference afterwards.

I am sorry to have put you to so much trouble, but if you were advertising your ponies at any time it would be of advantage to you to mention that you had the honour to supply the Royal Stables with the Pure Shetland Ponies.

9th January, 1888. From J. Duncan to Alexander Sandison:
... Dr Profeit said her Majesty was highly pleased with them. She sent the two gelded ponies to Windsor Castle and kept the larger of the two entires at Balmoral ... I have no doubt but that you may get more orders from them as Her Majesty has so many grandchildren, and so many gentry that would be fancying the ponies ...

19th January, 1888. From John Duncan to Alexander Sandison:
... I am sorry to hear mare ponies so scarce in Shetland, I could have got an order for a hundred of them from Lady Gordon Cathcart, to send to her estate in the West Highlands, where they intend to breed and establish a herd of them. The next time you come South be sure to call on me as I would like to see you.
                    With Best Wishes,

21st January, 1888. From Dr Profeit to Alexander Sandison:
                    Balmoral Castle Stamp
Dear Sir,
    I have to thank you very much for the shawl and gloves you were so kind in sending for my wife and self.
    The ponies were very much admired.
                    Yours sincerely,
                    Al. Profeit

5th August, 1899. From Shetland Agricultural Society to A. Sandison and Sons:
Gentlemen,
    I am in receipt of your letter of yesterday, regarding entries for the Show,
                    J. Wilson (Sec.)

Society and Personal

————

Lord George Sanger has purchased from Mr. George Stephen, 82 Regent Quay, Aberdeen, two beautiful Shetland ponies, to be presented by the Van Dwellers' Association to the Prince of Wales for the use of His Royal Highnesses' family.

—*From Aberdeen Daily Journal, June 28th, 1902.*

CHAPTER SEVEN

SARCOPTIC MANGE

It became obvious in February 1886 that there was a virulent scab disease affecting many of the ponies in Fetlar. The people of Fetlar were very dependent on the ponies for "flitting" their peats home in summer. The Local Authority was slow to act but the people took advice and this avoided the spread of the disease. Most of the Fetlar ponies were put down.

Flitting peats on Fetlar, c.1930.   © *Shetland Museum*

March 1886. From Gavin Hadden to Alexander Sandison:
> ... ponies for my wife's use – a pair of 42" to 43" mares 3 or 4 years old, free from Mange, black, bays or roans – must be the best in Islands, good action, small heads and perfect in every respect ...

April 1886. From Wm Henderson, Merchant, Burravoe to Alexander Sandison:
> ... I heard that Anderson Manson had the temerity to buy ponies from Fetlar when the disease is so fatal and of course at a low figure (one for 12/-)

14th May, 1886. From N. Duguid, Agricultural Department, Privy Council Office, Aberdeen to Alexander Sandison:

Sir,

I am directed by Professor Brown to inform you that on examination of a piece of skin you sent him he found the disease to be a form of mange due to the presence of a parasite but not the one usually found in the mange of the horse.

Will you kindly give Prof. Brown all the information you can on the following points:-

What is the history of the date and the origin of the disease?

What number of ponies are affected and over what extent of district or districts are they distributed?

What are the early symptoms of the disease and what parts of the skin are most affected?

Under what conditions are the ponies kept?

What is the average value of the ponies?

Will you send Prof. Brown a few pieces of skin about 3 or 4 inches square in some spirit so as to keep them from decomposing and enable him to examine the skin as fresh as possible,

I am Sir ...

24th May, 1886. From Alexander Sandison to Mr Duguid:

... acknowledge receipt of your letter of 14th Inst. The disease originated in the largest island of the Shetland group – Mainland, and I have written to a gentleman there as to the history and date of the origin of the disease, the early symptoms etc. I am also procuring from the neighbouring island of Fetlar a few pieces of skin, which I shall forward, preserved in spirits as directed, together with what information I can obtain as soon as received. The average value of the ponies is about £9.

The ponies are allowed to run at large on the common "scattald" and never stabled and never fed by hand unless during a long continued snowstorm in the winter season.

June 1886. From Agricultural Department to Alexander Sandison:

Sir,

The disease which you refer to in your letter of May 8th is clearly the one known as Sarcoptic Mange, that is to say the mange mites are true Sarcoptes or burrowing mites and are very difficult to destroy.

From the history which we have of the disease Prof. Brown concludes that there is no hope of eradicating it without the use of very stringent measures including slaughter of the worst cases and burial of the carcasses in quick lime.

Perfect isolation of all the diseased animals in order that proper remedies may be employed and obviously the animals which prove incurable must be destroyed.

Finally the effectual disinfection of all rubbing places and posts etc which the animals have been in contact is absolutely necessary to prevent the accession of disease when ponies are again let loose.

Professor Brown desires me to add that if the Local Authority think that any special powers are required to enable them to take the necessary steps and will state what their views are as to the scope and nature of these powers then application shall be carefully considered.

I am etc,

13ᵗʰ July, 1886. From Alexander Sandison to Major Cameron:

... I have fought against the taking of any horse stock out of Fetlar to Unst – indeed I intimated that I would lay hold of any and send them back, but they have been landed in Yell and carried by steamer.

As the Local Authority was so slow to act, Alexander Sandison and the Fetlar minister did what they could to limit the disease and avoid widespread disaster. In a letter from Major Cameron to Alexander Sandison in July he says:

Dear Sir,

I am glad that you and the minister of Fetlar have affected what the "Local Authority" could not. The Local Authority met and applied for special powers ... and Mr Hay expects the requisite order by first or second post when the same will be duly advertised etc, etc, as required by the Act. Until it arrived he did not see his way to putting warning notices in the papers because the Local Authority has, as yet, no power to enforce it.

Mr Hay today promised to speak to Mr Shand as to the S.S. Earl carrying ponies at all from one island to another ...

6ᵗʰ September, 1886. From Leonard Lyle M.P. to Alexander Sandison:

I have a letter from the Rev. J. J. Smith of Fetlar in which he speaks of the great distress prevailing on the island owing to the horse disease and the bad harvest of the year. He suggests an appeal to the public ... Require more information without which I could not make representation to the Scottish Secretary ...

1ˢᵗ June, 1887. From Colin Arthurson, Still, Fetlar to Alexander Sandison:

Mr Levie was here yesterday and declared our ponies free from disease ... (then he comments) – it pays them better to keep the disease lingering on for a while.

Four weeks later the Nicolsons were shipping their first ponies to Aberdeen since the outbreak of the disease. The majority of the Fetlar crofters' ponies had been wiped out. Carrying home the peats without the ponies proved to be crippling work. Anderson Manson and Alexander Sandison came to the rescue by putting in "halvers" mares. There are several letters from crofters requesting mares of which the following are samples.

Letters from Fetlar to Alexander Sandison or his son John.
From T. Jamieson, Houbie:

I hereby beg to apply for a mare pony on the terms you have given to G.H. Anderson and others in Fetlar. I am very anxious to get one.

Yours etc,

From Thos. G. Hunter:

Dear Sir,

I am aware that you have given ponies to some of the Fetlar crofters on certain conditions. I should be willing to take one on the same conditions anytime you have one to spare, hoping you will kindly put my name down on your list.

From Wm Petrie, Houl:

... Kindly put down my name in your list of Fetlar men wanting ponies in "Havers", as by doing so you will greatly oblige.

From George Brown:

... I had plenty of mares when the plague broke among them and I saved not one ...

From Wm Tulloch:

... my father had 16 head when the disease came in and now has none ... taking home the peats here without Ponies is a hardship unspeakable.

From Jerome Brown, Funzie. (re "halvers" request):

... for since I lost my old stock it made me a poor man. I lost 11 mares and 5 horses in prime or nearly so. I got 40/- compensation for the lot, but still I have not forgotten your goodness for what you did in trying to provide a cure.

Alexander Bandison Esq.   And. Nicholson
Uyeasound.

Lerwick 27th Feby. 1891.

Dear Sir,

Mr. Arthurson, Ground Officer for
Lady Nicolson informs me that in the first
week of December, his Shepherd found in
the Park of Urie, a mare having attached to
its mane, a piece of leather having thereon,
the words. "From Alexander Bandison", Uyeasound,
to James Coutts, Punzie, Fetlar". He informs me
that this pony must have been wilfully put
into the parks, and that similar acts have
previously taken place, and that it is necessary
in Lady Nicolson's interest to prevent repetition
of such encroachings. Mr. Arthurson instructs
me to demand the sum of Twenty Shillings,
as compensation for loss and damage caused
by your animal, being in the Park of Urie,
failing which an action will be raised
at the instance of Lady Nicolson.

I write this letter on the assumption
that the pony belongs to you.

Yours truly,
p. J Kirkland Galloway
And. Nicholson

The scheme had its problems.

49

1901. From Laurence Sinclair, Aiths Ness, Fetlar:
Dear Sirs,
I am shipping one horse this day three years old which I hope you will get all right. The price is £8.10/-. It is one from the mare I got from you.

January 1901. From Eliza M. Isbister, Aith, Fetlar:
I here enclose you £1 on the mare I have partly bought from you. She always travels away some distance from where we live, I think making for the place where she was landed. We fetch her home every day and feed her. She is very tame and anybody can go and take hold of Maggie.

May 1901. From Anderson Manson:
You will observe I am to have a sale of ponies from Fetlar on the 4th of June. These are all "Halvers" ponies. I intend on dividing and selling my portion as the people are over stocked.

From Thos G. Coutts, Funzie, Fetlar:
... They have been getting £6 to £6.10/- for three year olds and offering £3 for foals – but that does not matter. Will you please buy him for I have got into arrears of rent and they (the landowner) will take him by force – so will you please take him and send me half of his price and oblige.
Yours truly,

Often the "halvers" agreements came to the rescue when croft rents were high and incomes meagre.

1860. The following letter makes us realise how poverty stricken the crofters were at times:
Will you be as good as to send me a boll of oatmeal or flour, or if you have only a quarter, I am in such need, if ever pity touched your heart I trust you will send it. My husband (Laurence Sinclair) is at Greenland; you need not fear your pay as I have a young mare, the better of her is not in Fetlar ...

CHAPTER EIGHT

SPECIAL REQUESTS

Human nature being what it is, breeders have always been on the lookout for the unusual – either in colour or size. Others may strive to eliminate faults, establish certain bloodlines, look for perfect action or any combination depending on the emphasis placed by any individual. Although the Shetland pony is the purest of the native pony breeds its variations are endless. Some of the following letters show that the quest for small ponies didn't start yesterday.

1879. From Robert Borthwick, 2 Chiswell Street, London:
> ... I have a very small chestnut mare now, it is 6 years old and only 34 inches. I should be glad to match it if I was able ...

1882. From Alex Stephen:
> ... Have you any very small one ...
> ... one of them cream also a pair 40 inches which must be a match ...

1882. From George Stephen:
> ... 2, 3 year old mares, piebald or squebald ... also 2 as small as possible ...

1882. From J. Meiklejohn:
> Could you supply me with some nice mares. I would like black and bay ones and all sizes. If you have a good number I would come North and see them ...

1882. From Alex Stephen:
> ... 5, 18 month old mares of your smallest size ...

April 1886. From Margaret Henry, North Yell:
> ... about the horse betwixt you and me. He is 2 years old in the month of May and I have had the offer of £8 for him now. Please write me by the next post if I am to sell him for that ...

1882. From George Stephen:
> ... any fancy colour will do ...

1882. From Henry L. Weir:
> ... a pony that can do a mile in three minutes – one of three years old – a horse Pony preferred.

13th December, 1887. From Wm Angus, Ordinance Survey Offices, Reading:
> ... I must now congratulate you on your promotion in sending Shetland

Ponies to the Queen. I hope you are not now too proud to deal with a poor man.
... cost of the carriage of a pair of Shetland ponies from Shetland to London. Mrs Pearson speaks of having a pair. She is good for £1,000, if required.
... I am sorry to hear of the sad loss of life in Shetland last week, Whalsay seems to have suffered most but I suppose you had it in Unst as well.
(Comment on recent fishing disaster)

Ganson Brothers Lerwick, at one point had thirty six ponies for hire.

1882. From Ganson Bros., Lerwick (which began as pony carriage hirers and later became car and bus hirers):
> ... 10 - 15 small mare ponies, not over 38 inches, of a dark colour from 3 to 7 years and free of mange.

January 1889. From Jas. Duncan (one of the many communications from the Ladies Hope):
> I have a customer for the 35in. Mouse Mare provided she is not more than 35 inches and suits her. The Lady wants the pony sent to Leith and says:
> "If you find her the right height (35in) and would be willing to send her by steamer to Leith for me to see, should she answer the description I will at once send you my cheque."
> E. M. Hope.

November 1889. From Gavin Hadden:

> Enclosed I send you photos of "Tom Thumb" a black stallion, rising 5 years which I bought from you as a 2 year old. He is 37 inches and won third prize at the Highland Show last July; and of "Multum in Parvo" a dark brown rising 6 which I bought from Lord Londonderry. He was 2nd prize at the Highland Show this year – and also stands 37 inches.

With plans well underway for the formation of the Shetland Pony Stud Book Society, ponies' names are now frequently used – an added interest, as many of them are well known ponies.

25th November, 1889. From George Stephen:

> Please find enclosed cheque for £31.14.6. in payment for shawls and 4 ponies. They arrived safe and are good ones. They are for the Pantomime at the theatre here.

TELEGRAPHIC ADDRESS :—
"PONIES, ABERDEEN."

SHETLAND PONIES
FAMILY COBS & PONIES
PONY TRAPS & HARNESS
SHETLAND CALVER COWS

GEORGE STEPHEN
PONY SALE & EXCHANGE STABLES
32 James Street

Aberdeen 1st June 1892

6th December, 1889. From George Stephen:

> Sorry I did not know of the little horses before as I would have bought them for Her Majesty's Theatre in London where I have 10 little things for the Pantomime. Altogether I have 34 Ponies for Cinderella this season at various theatres. They are all supplied now and the first to start will be with your last foals. They will open on the stage on the 12th inst. I yoked them in the coach on Tuesday and they were first class.

30th December, 1889. From Gavin Hadden:

> ... I saw your 4 ponies in the theatre yesterday; they looked very nice.

Longcross House
Chertsey
Feb 5th 90   Surrey

Sir,
    I should be much
obliged if you would
give me particulars of any

extra small Shetland
ponies you may have
for sale, have you
any 4 years old ponies
35½ or less inches? Please
let me have full particulars
& lowest price at your
earliest.

                Yours truly
            Dorothea L Hope

5th Feb. 1890
D. L. Hope

The search for small ponies continues.

54

1882. From George Bruce to Alexander Sandison:

I have given G. Hadden £50 for "Tom Thumb" so our beauties are not losing favour.

1882. From Alexander Sandison to D. L. Hope:

Dear Madam,

I am favoured with yours of 5ᵗʰ inst. My smallest horse ponies are from 34 to 36 inches – two year olds and 36 to 28 inches – 3 year olds. The colours for the most parts are blacks and browns.

I have ponies four years old down to 34½ inches but these are kept for breeding purposes.

From D. L. Hope to Alexander Sandison:

Dear Sir,

I am much obliged for your letter about the ponies but a 2 year old at 34 inches is too large to suit me as when brought to England it would make a pony quite 37 or 38 inches at 4 years old. If, however you should be willing to sell the ponies that are under 35 inches please let me hear from you again as to lowest prices and particulars.

Yours truly,

6ᵗʰ January, 1890. From Gavin Hadden to Alexander Sandison:

... 2 good strong small young mares with good strong hocks and charge me what you like; I know you will be fair about this. I want them to cross with "Multum in Parvo" ...

8ᵗʰ February, 1890. Further:

... Thanks for sending the 2 mares which are nice ponies, well shaped and strong. You will be glad to hear I have sold "Tom Thumb" well, getting £50 for him; but of course he cost me a lot of money in very high feeding and expenses in sending him to shows etc. He is however a credit to your breeding and I tell everyone who bred him so it will do you good yet.

I sincerely hope you will not part with any quantity of your best brood mares, old or young:- Stick to them because we depend on you and other Shetland Breeders to keep the breed from running down and disappearing in America.

Have you any good stallions now ? if not I would strongly advise the purchase of a good one from Lord Londonderry; a big boned one with quality; it would pay you well.

Yours truly,

Gavin Hadden.

1882. From Alexander Sandison to Gavin Hadden:

... I have no doubt about "Mignon" being the sire of "Tom Thumb" and "Little Wonder" but as we kept no note of our ponies at that time cannot fix on the dam.

"Mignon" was a very fine pony and some of our best stock came from him. By a letter I had from Mr (Eli) Elliott last spring I learn he still has this pony.

Most letters were well written but occasionally I came across one like the following. Thank goodness they were not all as keen to save paper as W.H. McDougall of Bonnybrig.

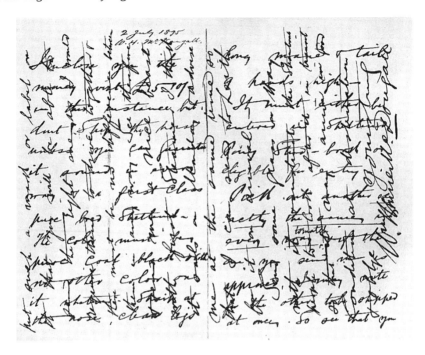

1891. From Chas. S. Guthrie:

... request to buy a small pony as advertised ... 22¼ inches as a foal (4 days old) weighing 27lb. [The dam was 34 inches and the sire 39½" inches]

January 1892. From Gavin Hadden:

... I offer to take your 32 horse ponies as per list, 39 inches and under at £13. ... particularly wish to receive "Saxie" and the other brown horse 34 inches with black points.

March 1892. From Gavin Hadden:

"Saxie" I might call a bright bay. General Gordon is a beautiful pony but not so small as you make him. He is a lovely rich bay colour.

1891. From Alexander Sandison to Gavin Hadden:

... "Dynamite" is entered as brown but from what you say about "Saxie's" colours, I fancy he will be bay ... they often change colour coming to their second year.

October 1890. From Alexander Sandison to George Georgeson, Cork:
...ponies are now both scarce and dear. Prices last paid for ponies rising 2 years to £10, for those rising 3 years £13 and up to £20 for specially fine stallions, and the smaller the size, if otherwise fine, the higher the price.

1891. From C. MacPherson Grant, Drumduan, Forres:
... "Little Dorrit", the brown mare (about 34 inches) and "Petite II" . If they are still for sale at prices mentioned by you viz £20 and £25, I shall be glad to take them myself.

July 1893. Further:
... I have bought from James Duncan two yearling mares which he purchased from you, said to be by "Norseman". Can you give me any information as to their dams ? If these can be traced in any degree I should be glad and if they belong to crofters I shall be happy to enter them at my own cost if they can be traced.

Also perhaps you will be good enough to say what horse "Veng" (which I purchased) was served by.

I have bought "Harold" from Lord Londonderry and hope he will do me good.

I have a good many of your breeding now – having lately bought 2 nice 3 year olds from Mr Hadden.

August 1893. And:
... I propose to call the one bred by Widow Sinclair foaled in April 1892 "April Shower" and the other bred by Robert Moar "May Morn".

E. GOODWIN PREECE,
Live Stock Agent
AND
Exporter.
ALL CLASSES OF STOCK SUPPLIED.

Telegrams: PREECE, Exporter, Shrewsbury.

3, Abbey Gardens,

Shrewsbury.   Nov. 27th. 189‑
ENGLAND.

E. A. Sanderson Esq.
    Uya Sound,
        Shetland, Scotland.

Dear Sir,

    I want 5 or 6 really good Shetland pony mares and one stallion.
I want good animals but can pay fancy prices. I shall be glad if you
will kindly quote me your price for the above f.o.r. where you buy them,
both for pedigree and non-pedigree ponies. The former must be entered
or eligible for entry in the Stud book. Please state their height.
        I am dear Sir,
            Yours faithfully,

                P. Goodwin Preece

Five or six very nice mares rising 3.yrs @ 9£
Stallion   —   —   —   10.10

Mares 3 + 4 yrs and supposed to be in foal £11
Stallion —   — £12 Colour of ponies black and
brown and all entered or eligible for entry
in Stud Book. Price £6.6. Stamme...

The demand for registered animals was growing.

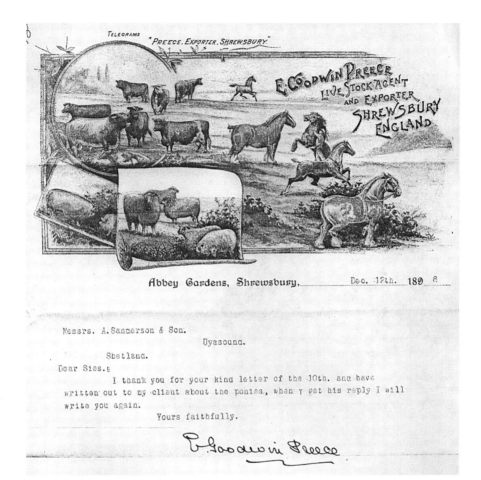

Abbey Gardens, Shrewsbury,   Dec. 12th. 189 8

Messrs. A. Sanderson & Son.
                    Uyasound.
        Shetland.
Dear Sirs,
        I thank you for your kind letter of the 10th. and have
written out to my client about the ponies., when I get his reply I will
write you again.
            Yours faithfully.

                        E. Goodwin Preece

An impressive letter heading.

1891. From Geo. B. Esselmont of Esselmont and Macintosh, 1 - 13 Broad Street, Aberdeen:
Dear Sir,
    I understand that your firm do an extensive business in Shetland ponies and, as I am starting a small choice stud write to ask what you have for sale. I saw at Mr Gavin Hadden's the other day a few two year olds which I understand came from you and you will understand what I want when I say they are about the quality required.
    ... further indebted if you would state which of the three stallions "Duke of Venice", "Puck" or "Dynamite" shows more bone and substance.

Dear Sir,

Would you kindly let me know if you would sell the mare and foal and what would be the price. If you have any more mares not exceeding 38 inches high you might let me know about them also. I mean the mare and foal that was advertised. The foal being 27¼ inches. Please let me know as soon as it is convenient

I am,

Yours truly,
James Macfarlane

The demand for the small ponies goes on.

March 1893. From Lady Dorothea L. Hope:

I have a mare pony 2 years old in May. She stands exactly 31½ inches at the withers. I should like to get one as small as this and the same age, do you think you could find me one? The little filly "Vesta" would have suited me but I cannot afford so big a price for so young a pony. I see by the Stud Book that she is only one year and five months old and will therefore grow enormously during the summer, being foaled in October. If she is exactly the 32½ inches I would give you £16 for her if you can accept my offer. [Also enquiries about "Mignon"]

March 1893. From Alexander Sandison to Lady Hope:

... authorised by the representatives of the late J. H. Mundell to offer for sale "Petite II" (560) Vol 2, and also her colt foal "Little Wonder". The latter was foaled in April '91 and is now only 31½ inches high.

This is a rare chance for securing a pair of ponies altogether exceptional for size and style.

I enclose a newspaper cutting describing "Little Wonder" at the age of four days.

Further:
"Mignon" was sold in 1888 to Mr Elliott, an American who has still got him as a stallion. This pony is one of the best I ever succeeded in breeding. "Petite II" is 34½ inches. The mare has a small well formed head, is heavy boned, has straight hocks and good action, but has never been trained. These particulars also apply to "Little Wonder" but his head is not so fine as his dams ... so far have failed to find a match for your small mare.

Further:
I accept your offer for the two ponies (£45) which will be shipped on Monday first.

April 1893. From Lady Hope:
The ponies have arrived safely last night ("Petite II" -35¼"). The colt is a pretty boy and has a neat head (32½").

September 1893. From Lady Hope.
"Petite II" is improving very much. I have had her feet well cut down and can now measure her exactly 35". The colt is also getting on well. He measures 33¼". If you have a mare to match "Petite II" please let me have full particulars and exact height.

November 1893. Further:
Dear Sir,
I am wanting a few Shetland ponies and should be glad to know what price you could supply me with nice ponies, mares or horse 2 years old, not exceeding 38 inches at 2 years. I do not want pedigree ponies but they must have neat heads and be in thriving condition and health.
Please let me know if you will sell "Constance" out of "Petite" (300) foaled '91 or "Petite III" out of "Petite" by "Sea King" (63) or "Little Dorrit" (130) by "Mignon". Kindly let me have exact heights by standard of the ponies mentioned and the price you will accept.
I am sorry to tell you we had the misfortune to lose the colt "Little Wonder". He died in a few hours of some poison which we could not discover. It will be a great loss. He was only 33 inches high and would have made a nice pony. Awaiting your reply re. the ponies.

November 1893. From Lady Hope:
... price of ponies now fully 2 years? Each pony costs me £2.10/- for freight and rail.

December 1893. From George Esselmont:
... I am anxious to secure a mare or stallion 3 to 5 years old which would stand a chance of winning the Highland Society's Show which you may be aware is to be held here in 1894.

December 1894. From Lady Hope:
Kindly send me particulars of the very smallest stallion you can supply me with. I want one 33 inches if possible, 4 years old.

1896. From J. Priestly Foster:

In Sept last year I bought at Lord Londonderry's sale a mare "Gold Medal" stated to have been bred by you. It is not entered in the Stud Book but if you could furnish me with particulars ...

1896. From W. H. McDougall, Bonnybrig, Midlothian. (One of a series of letters regarding ponies required following a visit to Unst.):

... You showed me a mare 37" high, 2 rising 3 yrs old, light brown with dark points named "Freda", dam "Freya" (329), sire "Oliver Cromwell" (77) price asked £10.

I think you told me this was either out of the same stock or a sister to some you had supplied to the Queen or some of her relations.

1896. From Sue Perceval, Lymington:

... would it be possible to change the little stallion "Midget's" name in the Stud Book to "Little Billie"?

1896. From James Sweeney, Co. Dougal:

... two swift well bred Shetland ponies for a little dog cart to drive the children to school.

1896. From George Stephen:

... So far as I can see the pony trade is at a discount here when everybody has a bicycle – then the folks who can now keep a pony will go in for them.

1897. From Alexander Sandison to his son Tom:

... I am glad Lady Hope is looking for ponies again. I consider her offer of £72 for the four ponies is not to be despised.

1897. From R. W. R. McKenzie, Earlshall, Leuchers:

Dear Sir,

Would you kindly send me particulars of any white or cream coloured ponies you may have for sale and oblige.

October 1897. From Alexander Sandison to R. W. R. McKenzie:

Dear Sir,

We are sorry we have no white ponies at present; we have, however, two pretty little mares, "Octavia III" and "Queen Bess II" – rising two years, both cream coloured.

Below are particulars of a few other ponies that probably may interest you:

1 nice four year old mare, brown and white. (in foal)

1 two year old mare, "Dorothea II", grey and white.

1 very nice mare, rising 2 years, grey with eel down back etc ... and besides the foregoing fancy coloured ponies we have handsome three and four year old stallions that we can highly recommend if you require such.

1897. From R.W.R McKenzie:

... Would you kindly give me the following particulars of the pair of cream coloured ones "Octavia III" and "Queen Bess II"; height, colour of eyes, mane and tail and price.

At this point Alexander was advertising in the *Farmer and Stock Breeder*.

March 1897. From Lady D. Hope, Skeynes, Eden Bridge:

... have only the two by stallions, "Mignon" and "Alister" by the first boat ... the telegraph clerk not knowing the name of Uyasound sent back my wire and so caused me considerable delay. [The Lady was not pleased]

I understand the price is £19 each.

One week later:

... the two entires have been delayed by storms ... I am to get for a lady a mare pony 4 to 7 years, 36 to 37 inches, warranted not in foal. She must not exceed £11 as the Lady has to pay the journey out to France which costs about £4 ... no pedigree is wanted, just for a pet.

One week on:

... the 2 entires arrived safely this morning. I think they are nice ponies and I enclose cheque in payment – £38. If you hear of any small ponies at any time I should be glad of particulars. I have them down to 33 inches but want something even smaller ...

1896. From Jas. Duncan:

... I am writing and sending quotations to a Russian who has asked me to send particulars of some ponies and should I have an order sent me I shall order some from your lists.

October 1897. To Gavin Hadden from Alexander Sandison:

... We have today shipped the ten ponies ... We would especially draw your attention to the bone and make of the "Cheries" and of "Irene II", "Freda", "Petite IV" and "Maid Marion" and "Ida" have also the making of prize ponies in them ...

From Gavin Hadden:

... I hear that "Cherie II" has a brown filly foal. Please say what is the sire.
[Below is written – "Cherie II" served by "Aladdin" 140.]

From Hunter Barr & Co, 27 Jamaica Street, Glasgow:

I am very glad you have succeeded in finding such a suitable trained pony for me and the character you get with it is worth a good deal ... I am greatly pleased with it.

7th March, 1898. To the Countess of Hopetown, Hopetown House, South Queensferry from Alexander Sandison:

> ... we have one that would be a very good match for "Freda". The pony is a good bay with black mane and tail, is strong and well made.
> 39¼ inches high and the same age as "Freda" ...

May 1898. From A. Agnew Ralson, Hopetown House, South Queensferry:

> ... I wired you this morning that Lady Hopetown would pay £14 for the pony to match "Freda" providing you took the risk of landing her safely to Leith.

15th March 1898 From Sue Perceval, Hinton House, Brackley, Northants:

> ... if you have any mare ponies, very small about 2 years old and for sale. They must be small, well bred, small heads and good straight legs, in the S.P.S.B. or eligible for the same ...
>
> I have the little bay mare "Snowdrop" (you sent me two years ago) and she is a very nice one ... The horse pony grew too big and had such weak hocks so I sold him.

Mrs Perceval was in luck as far as the small mare was concerned. The following appeared in *The Shetland Times* on the 1st May, 1998, in the "100 years ago" column.

100 YEARS AGO

On Saturday last the SS. *Earl of Zetland* had down from Baltasound one of the smallest of small Shetland ponies, supplied from the well-known stud of Messrs Sandison & Sons, pony-breeders, Unst. The pony was supplied to a lady in England, and is we believe one of the smallest of its age that ever left the island.

The following particulars about the pony may be read with interest, but no amount of writing could convey an idea of this wonderful piece of horse-flesh, as it had to be seen to be appreciated.

It is a mare pony Effie II, dam Effie (1141), sire Dynamite (114). Her height is 30½ inches, and she weighs 132 pounds. She was a dark dun colour approaching black, and was most perfectly formed in every detail. Such a pony should prove the pride and envy of show yards in the south.

"Effie II" was on her way to Mrs Perceval. The mare was two years old at the time.

24th March. Further:
... please send me all the particulars of the little dun mare "Effie II"

"Effie II" born 1896

Sire	G.P.	G.G.P. BLACKIE
DYNAMITE (114) Born 6/5/1890 Dk Brown 37¼"	TRIPTOLEMUS (45)	GROGA
	ZOE (367)	
Dam		BLACKIE
EFFIE (1141) Born 16/5/1892 Brown 37"	NESTOR (29)	PORTIA (356)
		PRINCE
	MINNIEHAHA (354)	LADY GERALDINE (351)

7th May:
... so enclose cheque £15 for the little mare "Effie II", I am pleased with her.

17th May:
... "Effie" is very well and a dear little pony.

However a letter in March 1900 from S. Perceval states:
... I am sorry to tell the very best pony you sold me "Effie II" by name, if you remember her, died this winter from influenza followed by something internal; it was a great grief to me as she was such a dear little beauty.

1899. In this year there were nine letters from Lady D. Hope. They speak for themselves.

March:
... will you send me the particulars of "Trilby". I am driving now a mare bred by you "Irene II" (since called "Kelpie"), a very good pony to go but plain head.

I include the Sandison letterhead at this stage to show the diversity of the business.

ALEXANDER SANDISON & SONS.

TELEGRAPHIC ADDRESS:—
SANDISONS, UYASOUND.

MERCHANTS.

FISH CURERS.

SMACK AND BOAT
OWNERS.

MANUFACTURERS
OF
SHETLAND HOSIERY
AND
LACE GOODS.

FLOCKMASTERS
AND
GRAZIERS.

BREEDERS
OF
SHETLAND PONIES.

....DEPARTMENT.

UYASOUND,...
SHETLAND.

February 22nd., 1902.

CIRCULAR.

April. To Lady Hope from A. Sandison and Sons:

... A pure bred Shetland pony 46 inches high cannot be procured, we do not think it exists. However we think we may be able to get a pony such as you describe from the stud of Sir Arthur Nicolson, Fetlar. There is a strain of Arabian blood in these ponies and they are considerably larger than the pure bred Shetlanders ...

May. From Lady Hope:

... you say "Erna's" foal is 23 inches, our smallest this year is 22 inches, 28½ lbs but two years ago we had one 20 inches, weight 30 lbs.

This colt is now 2 years past and just 31 inches.

Please do not let any of the mares be served before leaving Shetland a I want to put "Lucy" to the 31 inch horse, and the other two mares I do not want in foal.

If you are down South again we should be so pleased if you would come down and see our stud.

June:

... "Trilby" goes well in harness ...

July:

... we did well in Edinbro ...

July:

... we were very pleased to get 1st with the colt we bred ourselves only 31¼ inches at 2 years and 2 months old. Also his dam was first and we think her the best mare we have ever seen – altogether we have had an extraordinary good year in the show ring having won at six shows – 11 first prizes, 6 seconds, one third and the reserve for the Prince of Wales medal. I hope your Shetland show will be a success and we only wish we could come up for it.

July:
... £45 for "Lucy", "Trilby" and "Erna" and £15 for "Imogen II".

August:
... we want to sell "Picotee" sire "Champion", dam your mare "Petite II" (568) – rich brown, 35 inches and had the most extraordinary bone and a nice short back, like his mother. He is 2 years old but made up like a 5 year old – £25.

1899. From Miss Chicester, Arlington Court, Barnstable:
She (Miss Chicester) will send you a cheque for £24 for "Fairy II" and "Olivia III". Those she bought from the Ladies Hope are about 33 inches.

Further:
... received the ponies and is pleased with what she sees of them.

1899. From Geo. Laurence and Co., General Merchant, Ulsta, Yell:
I have got "Udaller" (stallion)here all right and enclose £12 in payment ... Kindly send the particulars of his pedigree as I do not have any of the Stud Books.

1899. From George Stephen:
Ponies arrived safe – nice ponies. The greyish foal was very bad last night. I gave her a half pint of bass and about a gill of brandy mixed. She is alright this morning. I don't know if she comes of a teetotle family but the good stiff dram seems to have agreed with her.

Further from George Stephen:
... Where the pair of chestnut horses were foaled and their history, and also their pedigrees. They are away to a good home and I said they were bred on the most North Easterly point of Her Majesty's dominions in this country where there is no tree to be seen or shelter of any kind etc, etc. Am I right in this?

I think I also said the herd they came from were the oldest known, etc, etc.

He says they were not 3 years old but after a bit of bother I got the cash. This means everything. I did not look at the mare's mouth but did the horse and his teeth were up nicely and only an ass or a schoolboy could have said he was anything but a 3 year old. I never handled a nicer little lot. I am just going to wire you about the Fetlar ponies. I can do with 6 to 10 yearling mares – good ones and good colours.

1904. From Jas. H. Laurenson, Fetlar to J., P. Sandison:
... be so good as to send us a stallion in place of "Dynamite".

1904. From A. Fiddes (Minister) to J. P. Sandison:
... as his children are becoming 'heavies' he would like a heavier and stronger animal for driving his children to the Tain Academy ... a suitable animal at your leisure either on the island home or on the adjoining island, say on Nicolson's Estate, Fetlar. Mr Hamilton told me once that crosses were to be had on that island.

May 1905. From Shetland Pony Stud Book Society:
... I am disappointed to have no entries from you for Vol XV. I would be glad if you could send me your entries by return of post as it would be very disappointing to miss your entries after all those years you have contributed so much to the success of the society.

1907. From R. W. R. MacKenzie, Earlshall:
... require for a special purpose a grey colt, filly or mare – think you have some colour registered. It must be shapely, eligible for Stud Book, showing no white horn on the hoofs and with the bluish Arab like skin at the muzzle.

EARLSHALL,
LEUCHARS,
FIFE.

24th Oct 1904

Dear Sir,

I am obliged for yours of 19th inst offering me two grey yearling colts at £8 each. F.O.B. You do not give their names or pedigrees, nor can I know one grey colt (who produce of Lady (2101)) among your 1906 entries. Of course you will understand the colour I want is genuine grey not cream or dun. However if the two colts you offer are fully pedigreed, straight in their legs, and like growing beyond stud book height I will give you the price asked.

I want them for an experiment in colour breeding. I should have preferred females. Have you no grey foals this year?

Yours faithfully,
R W MacKenzie.

P.S. If you are disputching the colts you will advise me how I take them. If I could have picked up a few more they might all have come together.

By genuine grey I mean the grey that turns white with age.

1907. From Blanche Huband (looking for cream ponies):

> ... also any in foal mares for sale with "Lord of the Isles", "Prince of Thule"
> and "Jack" in their pedigrees.

From A. Sandison and Sons to Blanche Huband:

> ... we have arranged to ship three colts, "Hamilear" (cream), "Nebo" (grey)
> and "Carol" (black) ... 3 pedigree colts rising 2 years – £27 ...

(Strict instructions were given to the Steamboat Agent in Lerwick that ponies
were to be loose in a pen and properly fed and watered.)

October 1907. From Harry Holmes (H. and M. Smith Ltd.):

> ... I consider "Emeer" the best pony for stud purposes that was at the
> Earlshall sale and since I got him I am more convinced of this than ever. He
> has got a far better body and shoulder on him than others and if you wish
> him I will let you have him for £20 sterling f.o.b. Aberdeen subject to being
> unsold on hearing from you.

October. Further:

> Thanks for your letter of the 26th covering cheque and I am also glad to
> notice that the pony arrived in good order and working well. I wish you luck
> with him.

October 1907. From Gavin Hadden, Levant Lodge, Earls Groome, Worcester:

> ... I was sorry not to have another talk with Mr Sandison (J. P. I believe) at
> Earlshall last month.

1907. From George Hendry (sec to S.P.S.B.S.):

> I observe that the filly foal of "Vordillaide" which you have entered as
> additional produce is sired by "Adonis", the sire of the dam. Is this correct?

CHAPTER NINE

THE AMERICAN TRADE

The first mention of the American demand I could find was an article in *The Shetland Times*, 20th October, 1873, and a letter from J. Corey in 1874. Eli Elliott made three trips to Shetland in the eighties, his third consignment of 129 being the largest that had ever gone to America to one individual. A report in the local paper on his return stated:

> Eli Elliott came in Saturday night all the way from the Shetland Islands and brought with him pretty much all the merchantable ponies the Islands contained. The pony ranch presents a sight now worth going many miles to see – 140 frisky, lively little rascals, among them "Yum Yum" a pony 31 inches and fully grown. These ponies are wading around in better pasture than they ever dreamed of seeing on their native heath. They present a spectacle of calm contentment pleasant to behold.

The ponies were strictly for children's ponies and pets. There was apparently a financial depression in the 1890s when the trade tailed off a little and bicycles became "the thing". Eli Elliott was one of the main instigators of the American Shetland Stud Book which was first published in 1893. Unfortunately it branched off into a "new improved" Shetland pony which bears little resemblance to the original, being crossed with hackneys.

Below is the article from *The Shetland Times* mentioned above:

UNST – SHETLAND PONIES FOR AMERICA – 1873

Shetland ponies are world known, and there must be few climes where some member of the species is not to be met with. They appear to be the "Tom Thumb" of the genus Equus, but unlike dwarf in general, for symmetry, high spirit, and that exquisite instinct which borders on something higher, if indeed intelligence be not its proper designation, but few of their larger brethren can excel them. Of course, as dealers are generally more anxious to secure cheap than finely formed animals, it is not often that the droves, which leave our shores, contain many very fine animals, and they are oftener more remarkable for their shaggy wildness than for their neatness and beauty. A shipment of a very different order, however, has just been made. Mr J.G. Corey, of Suisun City, California, U. S. A., wishing to introduce our miniature horses into that vast and rich State, came over to our isle to make a personal selection. Mr Corey, we understand, would only purchase first-class animals, and for those he was willing to give a liberal price, the result being that he secured the finest lot of ponies we ever remember having seen leaving this isle. They were all young animals, mares of one and two years old, and two very fine stallions. On the possession of one of the latter, we think we may congratulate Mr Corey, he having procured, in our opinion, the finest pure

Shetland stallion* to be had anywhere in these islands. It is the well-known one from the stock of Mr Craigie, Lund, which has whenever exhibited, obtained highest honours – having, in three years, carried off eight first prizes. The perfect symmetry of this beautiful animal is such that it may compare with the ideal perfection portrayed in the Elgin marbles. And the price, almost fabulous, paid by Mr Corey is, we understand, the highest that has ever been given for any Shetland horse sold in this country. The other stallion from Mr Sandison, Gardiesfauld, was also very fine. From this gentleman's stock, he also purchased the brown mare whose small size and handsome form we noticed in our report of the Unst Agricultural Society's Show. We wish Mr Corey and his purchases a prosperous voyage across the Atlantic, and a pleasant ride over the great plains.

Another writer states: The Chieftain's Bride, on her last Monday trip shipped from Unst a valuable cargo of cattle and sheep purchased by Mr A. Duncan of Aberdeen. Of the cattle we observed two shorthorn bulls, one of which, a two-year-old that carried the first prize at the Unst Agricultural Show, was sold by Messrs Jaffray and Spence for the respectable sum of £36. A few of the Unst farmers are becoming noted for the superior quality of their stock. The other day, Mr Craigie of Lund sold a small pony, pure Shetland breed, for £30, to a gentleman from California. The little beauty had taken double prizes at the last Show, and will no doubt attract attention when it reaches its destined Californian home.

Shetland Ponies are in such demand and at most fabulous prices, that it becomes doubtful whether sheep or ponies are the safest for the farmer. At present the balance inclines in favour of ponies.

* This stallion had been bred in Unst from a mare belonging to Mr Edmonston, Buness and his sire belonged to Mr W.G. Mouat, Springfield.

September 1874. From John G. Corey, San Beuno Ventura, California to Alexander Sandison:

Dear Sir,

Your interesting letter of August 12th was duly received and we were all glad to hear from you.

Since returning from your far off islands the letter received from yourself and others from different parts of the Archipelago as well as a weekly paper from Lerwick (*The Shetland Times*) keeps my memory fresh and at times causes almost a desire to visit you again.

The reasons for visiting you last time may be summed up in a few words. I had been engaged in Merchandising for seven year past as Ironmonger and our place is suddenly 'used up' as we say in our country by a Railway being built very close by us but the town Authorities and the Railway Co were at loggerheads and could not agree. The Railway Co caused other towns to be built up on both sides and the Co discriminated in their favour and against us. In the consequential war, our town went down and property owners suffered great losses in depreciation of property. The merchant business fell off and a general stagnation followed and my sales declined from $33,000 to $13,000 annually and my property fell from $3,000 to $1,000.

71

I had also suffered ill health ... After selling out and partially collecting my debts I was prevailed upon to make the trip to Europe and the speculation of Importing Shetland ponies was conjured up by my friends as a novelty and one that would be a profitable venture. The result was in many respects a success ... my health was so much improved ...

Your question as to whether Shetland Ponies would sell in New York will be answered hereafter. I will write to acquaintances there and answer as soon as I hear from my friends.

In case you could sell a small lot in New York one of your sons could make the trip in three weeks from Shetland to New York. The most troublesome and expensive part of the trip I made was from New York to California. I was compelled to have about 30 to fill a 'car' and Rail Roading with stock is costly and attended with loss. The trip could be made from your place to New York without losing a single pony and would only be a pleasure for one of your sons.

I am purchasing a tract of land. I will probably begin with 1,000 to 1,200 good breeding ewes ... wages for herders is £5 to £6 per month. Sheep are worth 8/- to 12/- per head for common grades. The average yield of wool 7lbs and is worth 7½d for full clip and 10 to 12d for spring clip ...

At this time I have not got an opportunity of getting a Post Office order on Great Britain and will delay sending for knitted goods until some future time ...

Tell Bella her little pony is the pet of Dr H. H. Touland's son, (San Fransisco) an eminent surgeon and is much prized.

I remain as ever,
Your sincere friend,

('car' – American carriage which could take from 30 to 50 ponies)

March 1879. From J. Meiklejohn:
... I sent you a good man last week and I was glad to hear that he broke ice with you and I hope you may soon become a large exporter to the U.S.A.

Yours truly in haste,

June 1879. From D. A. Cremer, American Horse Depot, 184 Regent Rd, Liverpool (orders a shawl):
... Me Shuklim wishes me to say how much you will take for 20 or 30 head of Shetland ponies from 30 to 40 inches in height – he only wants a few geldings and more stallions than mares (1 third mares) ... He was on his way to your place last month but found 20 head at Stephen's ...

Please put the price right as he thinks he can open quite a trade with you for ponies.

14th June, 1883. From J. M. Flowers to John P. Sandison:
Since receiving your telegram I have purchased a Blue horse same age as yours also mares enough to complete the number that I intend taking with me so please send my 13 ponies by returning steamer as I must be in London to ship by the steam ship which sails from London to New York on the 22inst.

1886. From James Duncan, Inverness to John P. Sandison:
My Dear Sir,
A Yankee wants quotations for 6 or 8 small Shetland ponies, mares and horse 2 to 4 years old. Height, age, colour and price of each.

30th September, 1886. From H. J. Ritter (staying at a hotel in Glasgow) to Alexander Sandison:
... I hope you have selected me good strong, healthy ponies ... the other lot landed in good condition.

11th October, 1886. Further:
... payable to you order for £103.15/-. I expect to ship Friday and will have 80 Shetlands.

24th December, 1886. From George Stephen:
... I have just returned from America ... I require 12 to 20 first class mare ponies not over 39 inches rising 2 for delivery at the end of January ...

June 1887. From Wm. Rowles, Ontario:
... I would like to get a car load if I could get them cheap enough to make a profit on them ... could you ship me a car load ... handsome ones not more than eight years old ... I would like one or two good colts for stallions.
A note below says: 2 yr old horses £9.
                          3 or 4 yr old horses £13.
                          Mares not to be had.

In a letter to James Duncan in December 1887 Alexander says:
... mares are very scarce. The Yankees bought all that could be got in Shetland and the disease cleared out Fetlar so it will be some time before there are many to sell.

1886. From Eli Elliott & Co., West Liberty, Iowa:
... When we visited you late August and you had nothing but a few very good stallions for sale – you told us you would have 20 or 30 two and three year old mares for sale in the spring of 1888 also some stallions.
... We were very favourably impressed with the stock on your Island and will hope to hear from you ... subject to approval on our arrival over ...

December 1887. From James Duncan, Fern Villa, Inverness:
... A Yankee has written me asking prices for 10 to 12 Shetland ponies, Horses and mares – young ones for breeding ...
You have had the honour of supplying Her Majesty with ponies lately. I wish I had been so fortunate.

ELI ELLIOTT & CO.

IMPORTERS AND BREEDERS OF

Shetland, Exmoor, Welch and Indian

PONIES.

January 1888. From Eli Elliott & Co:

... We will want a few choice stallions and can no doubt pick them out of your lot. We want to bring out an Importation of really choice ones as the "best are always the cheapest" before one gets through with them.

4th May, 1888. Further from Edinburgh:

... We landed here safely after making a purchase of some ponies of Mr Wm. Manson so we now have 126 head.

We succeeded in getting pasture for them 12 miles from here on the way towards Glasgow at 2/6 per head and attendance on them free.

April 1888. From Caledonian Railway Company, Eastern Section, Edinburgh:

... our present rate for Shetland ponies from Leith to Liverpool is £4.10/- per wagon at owners risk ...

April 1888. From Leyland and Co., Liverpool:

... we shall be pleased to carry your ponies to Boston at £2.10.0 each ... you have to put up fittings or we would do so if required and debit you with cost of same. Ship provides water only and you finding fodder and attendance ... cattle men are constantly returning to Boston by our Steamers and we suggest you make arrangements with one of them.

The American trade was not without it's problems.

1888. From J. C. Stevenson:

... Since the arrival of my ponies on the 30th May I have been most unfortunate with them. The Distemper has been most prevalent here this spring – out of the lot of 12, 5 have died. The remainder were so reduced as to be marketless till next spring.

(Influenza affecting 'green' ponies not acclimatised.)

I paid the man in charge $10 for looking after them on the voyage. He asked from you as well as me, £5 or $25 but I gave him $10.

Mr Elliott of Iowa lost 11 ponies on the voyage and he has the hardest part of the journey before him.

I do not think the Leyland line is at all a good one to bring out stock by. They put the ponies in old cattle pens and charged me with new stalls and the ponies were next to the Donkeys. The galley was there and it was always too hot.

The ponies you sent I must say, were the makings of good ones – that pair of bays will bring $300 next spring.

(£150 for the 10 mares and 2 stallions)

December 1888. From Eli Elliott:

Dear Sir,

Your letter of 15th inst is to hand. We can not ask you to keep the ponies for us if a good opportunity should arise to sell them, as our needing them is a matter of doubt just at present as we have only sold about half a score of all we brought home – trade seems very slow but now our election for president is past we hope for a better demand ...

... It is with the greatest of sorrow that I must tell you of the death of my cousin Mr Smith who was with me at your place – it occurred at his home in Virginia the last of August. He imported a French stallion and a pair of mares and the stallion kicked him in the breast, breaking his breast bone from which he died a week later. He went behind the horse and put his hand on him without the horse knowing of his presence ...

1890. From G. Bruce, Royal Northern Agricultural Society, 35 Market Street:

I enclose copy of certificate of "Tom Thumb" and will feel obliged if you can give me his pedigree, or at least as much as you can as he is to be a 'Stud' horse for the American lot.

P. S. I am getting "Tom Thumb" sketched and a painting purchased.

October 1890. From Eli Elliott, Iowa. [More problems]:

... out of 65 Shetland mares bred in 1889 I got but 4 living foals – an epidemic caused the loss of many thousands of dollars worth of foals in this state.

I will want 25 to 30 good Shetlands in the spring and write to ask what you furnish them at in Glasgow or in Montreal, Canada, the latter very much preferred. I want black; don't object to piebald or grey; don't want yellow dun – want them in good condition not over 42 inches and as small as you can get them. I want, if I can get 30 head, about 5 stallions and I want two stallions well marked Black and white 38 to 40 inches.

The black one Bertie Anderson got off you for £20 and sold to me, I still keep in my own stud. I also have several of the very small mares but they are now nearly all over 36 inches. Do you know of a very wee one – I want one smaller than anyone else has if I can find him or I would like two of them, I want part of these mares to put in my own breeding stud as I have sold down till I have but 32 Shetlands.

I see you have, or are getting a Stud Book for Shetlands on your side as well as me on this side. This will be a deadner to some Scotch pony men that I could name and it is a move in the right direction. We are very careful on this side that nothing but the best – those worthy of perpetuating in kind – get into the Stud book – they must not only be pure Shetlands but worthy individuals also ...

How many ponies do you think there are in the Shetland Islands all told ?

In his reply Alexander Sandison estimates the number at about two thousand, a vast decrease from the ten thousand estimated fifty years previously, but not surprising considering the huge demand by the pit trade and the later American trade.

October 1890. From George Stephen:

... I have just returned from America ... I had 102 ponies with me ...

November 1890. From Alexander Sandison to Eli Elliott:

... Shetland ponies have been getting dearer and dearer ... parties began to buy foals only 6 months old at £6 and now £7 is freely paid for them. Mr Watkins from America was in Shetland last week and bought a lot chiefly from the Marquis farm at Bressay and gave very large prices I understand ...

As to very wee ones we have a few very small ponies but don't care to sell any of them just now as we are trying to breed some of the smallest.

1890. From Gavin Hadden:

An American asks particularly about the pedigree of a very small brown stallion which you sold to me as a 3 year old 2 years ago.

... meantime I am, by small degrees raising a stud of my own, founded principally on Lord Londonderry's stock and which is extra large boned and of small stature, miniature Clydesdales.

March 1902. From A. Sandison and Sons to Gavin Hadden:

... We notice what you say with the reference to the restrictions on the exportation of young ponies to the United States. Before the "McKinley Tariff" came in force any pony that was entered in the Stud Book was eligible but since then certain restrictions have been imposed ... no doubt Mr Ross would be able to give you full information on this point.

NOTICE TO SHIPPERS.

WHITE STAR LINE OF STEAMERS,
LIVERPOOL TO NEW YORK.

Shippers are respectfully informed that the Steamship "NARONIC" *will be despatched for* NEW YORK <u>DIRECT</u>, *on Friday, the 2nd December.*

Loading Berth—West Side Alexandra Dock.
Rates of Freight from Liverpool:—

Fine Goods	12 6	*per ton measurement,*
Fustians, Carpets and Calf Hairs	10/-	*& 10 per cent. primage.*

All packages should be plainly marked with the name of country of origin, to comply with the requirements of the United States Tariff Law.

Sample Packages should bear Consignees' full Address in addition to any other distinguishing marks put on.

Accommodation for HORSES, PONIES, SHEEP, and all descriptions of LIVE STOCK, unsurpassed by any Vessel afloat.

APPLY TO

ISMAY, IMRIE & CO,

10, Water Street,
Liverpool, 22nd November, 1892.

To follow—"BOVIC," December 9th.
„ "RUNIC" December 16th.

One of the shipping lines supplying a regular service.

1893. From Alexander Sandison to Gavin Hadden:

... I sold all my Stud book yearling mares for export to America last year with the exception of two or three which I kept for breeding purposes.

1898. To Blackwell Sons & Co, The Albany, Liverpool from A. Sandison and Sons:

... can give you a selection at anytime from our 200 ... yearlings – £6, 2 yr olds – £8, and 3 yr olds – £10, all from pedigreed stock ... principal colours black and brown

1900. From Anderson Manson, Maryfield, Bressay:

... how many 2 to 3 year old mares, pedigreed eligible for export to America free of duty and what price?

1900. Further:

Can you supply me with some piebald mare ponies, pedigreed for free export to America?

Only pedigreed ponies could now enter the States free of charge and people who failed to register their ponies were now losing out on this lucrative market.

1905. From George Stephen:

... I hope you had a good turn from the American – he had a deal of bother on the other side with the pedigrees and had to pay a lot of money Duty. Some of the Pedigrees he got were for stock sent over before.

The following are some enquiries from America.

M. H. LANE, PRESIDENT
F. B. LAY, VICE PRES. AND TREAS.
V. L. PALMER, SECRETARY

FINE
CARRIAGES AND
CUTTERS

MICHIGAN BUGGY CO.

WE POSITIVELY DO NOT SELL CATALOGUE HOUSES
DIRECTLY OR INDIRECTLY

KALAMAZOO, MICH. Nov. 3, 1904.

A. Sandison,

Uyasound,
Shetland Isles, Scotland.

Dear Sir:-

We are large breeders of Shetland ponies.
We have 125 of all ages on hand now. We sell about 50
to 100 ponies annually. We had thought of trying to
import a bunch of several carloads, providing we can
buy them cheap enough. We would want for every 25
mares a good stud; and we would want registered stock,
so that we could get them through free of duty for
breeding purposes. Possibly we could buy the North
of Scotland wild mountain ponies cheap enough, so that
we could afford to pay the duty.

If we bring over a 100 or more ponies, we
will sell what we have on hand, and use the imported
ponies for breeding purposes. Will you have the kind-
ness to give me all the information you can about all
classes of Shetland, Welsh and Iceland ponies, and
the best place to buy any and all kinds of ponies.

The pony business is only one branch of our
business. We are very large manufacturers of all
styles of carriages, sleighs, pony vehicles, etc. We
would like to sell you anything we manufacture at the
lowest wholesale price.

An early reply, with all the information
you have on the subject of pony business will be
very much appreciated.

Very truly yours,

G

RIVERSIDE PONY FARM.

P. S. We enclose herewith return envelope. We would
gladly have prepaid this, but we cannot get British stamps
here.

79

London, England.   3 Waterloo Place, W.
                                Dec: 2nd 1904.

Messrs A. Sandison & Sons,
    Uyasound,   Shetland.

Dear Sir,

        I am refered to you by P. P. Ross Esq., Sec. of the Shetland Stud

Book Society, as breeders of Shetland Ponies.   I am interested in

the purchase of some such ponies for a large farm in Pa. U. S. A.

We shall need registered stock, not over the hieght allowed by the

Shetland Stud Book rules, as near 36 inches as possible.   We wish

them for breeding purposes, and would like them to shew good ancestry.

Those that I wish to buy should be accompanied by certificates of

pedigree, signed by the Sec. of the Shetland Stud Book, shewing
                         previous
their ancestors for two generations, who have been registered so that

we can have such certificates vised by the U. S. Consul at the port

of Shipment so that we can have them shipped duty free.   If you have

any good stock such as we need kindly let me know the particulars,

and prices, as soon as possible, Upon receiving your communications

I will write you the wishes of the party in America who need them.

                                Yours resp'y
                                Henry M. Hall

August 1905: The S.S. *Queen* chartered by Messrs George H. and Fred
Simpson of Chicago U.S.A. shipped at various ports in Shetland a record number
of 213 Shetland Ponies destined for America.

The order for this big consignment was placed in the hands of Mr Peter
Anderson, Globe Buildings, Lerwick, and the purchases were made by him
throughout the county from all the well known stud farms including:
Mr John Bruce, Sumburgh
Messrs Anderson Manson and Peter Manson of Maryfield and Laxfirth
Messrs A. Sandison and Sons
Mr John Keith, West Sandwick
Mr J. Craigie, Ordale
Mr Peter Anderson himself and a number of crofters.
The *Queen* proceeded to Aberdeen where the ponies were re-shipped on one
of Messrs Thomson's liners going to Philadelphia. Messrs Simpson had appointed
Mr Anderson to be their agent in Shetland and purchase more ponies.

CABLE ADDRESS
"ACMEFOOD" CHICAGO
A. B. C. CODE

T. C. SIMPSON, PRESIDENT
W. H. EVANS, SECRETARY
GEO. H. SIMPSON,
TREAS. AND GEN'L MGR.

ACME POULTRY FOOD

110 LA SALLE ST.

TELEPHONE MAIN 2370

We are the exclusive
manufacturers
of
ACME FOOD
and
ACME POULTRY FOOD.

Many of our local
dealers' sales exceed three
carloads a year.

76—76
Champion Sweep-Stakes
and
High Class Prizes
awarded
ACME FOOD
fed animals at the
International Stock Show,
Chicago, 1900.

80—80
for the year 1901.

200—200
for the year 1902.

We are
the Owners
of
LADY ACME,
Largest Cow
in the World.
Weight 3450 lbs.
Fed
ACME FOOD.

ACME FOOD
is fed and recommended by
Live Stock Commission
Men from all markets,
as well as the
best Feeders and Breeders
the country affords.

ACME FOOD
is fed to all classes
of stock and at all times
with safety and as
a profit.

ACME FOOD
produces fat and flesh
and substitutes
Oil Meal
at one-third the cost.

ACME FOOD
PAYS TO FEED.

ACME POULTRY FOOD
produces eggs in cold
weather and
prevents disease that poultry
are heir to.

SOLD ON GUARANTEE.

In reply refer to File 2952   CHICAGO, Feb. 3, 06

Alexander Sandison & Sons,

Unasound,
Shetland Islands.

Gentlemen:---

Wish to inquire what Ponies you have for sale.
Will say, that I can use any Ponies that can be
imported duty free at the same prices that I paid you
last year. However, would not care for any Stallions,
although, could use some if they were good.
We want to buy what we term, full carload lots
that is, 45 to 55 head, as we can ship that many in our
American cars (Carriages) from the Sea-port to Chicago.
I am not particular in regard to buying Mares above 5
years of age, in fact prefer the younger ones. Could use
a car-load if you could arrange to furnish me with that
number.
In the event that you can accept of my offer
can Cable to me as per the address above (ACMEFOOD,
Chicago. Accepted) or use any of the Codes, and would be
well to state what month that you could ship, and follow
this up by a letter advising the manner in which you wish
the payments arranged.
Anticipating the favor of your reply, and trust
that you will be able to supply me with some more Ponies,
I am.

Very truly yours,

GHS/MP

TELEGRAPHIC ADDRESS.
"ANDERSON, HILLSWICK"

From
John Anderson & Sons.
Hillswick,
Shetland, N.B.

17th Feby. 1906.

To Messrs Alex Sandison
Sons,
Uyeasound.

Dear Sirs, Today we wired you as undernoted, the same
is herely confirmed viz:—
"Have letter from Simpson Chicago says written you also please
" do not reply until you get our letter posted today. Anderson.

As Simpson mentioned having written you, as well as
ourselves, we thought, that as the number of
Duty Free Pedigreed Ponies, is limited, it might
do no harm for us, to understand each other,
in regard to the price, we should accept for this
class during season 1906— and you can, if
you think proper advise us what prices you
intend to ask, and stick to for.
Colts & Fillies, foaled 1905.
    ditto   "   1904,
Mares, foaled 1899 to 1903.
If however you think it better each should
act independant of the other, please send
a telegram on receipt— just "independant," &
we shall understand. We omit to say that
Simpson suggests last years prices—
Since we are writing, have you any good
Pedigreed Stallions for sale at a reasonable
price, 5/10 years old: or any rising 4 or older
Horse Ponies 41/45 inches which you can offer us.
Yours truly,   John Anderson & Sons

March 1906. To George Simpson, Chicago:
... sorry we have no pedigree ponies over one year for sale. We have however, 20-25 pedigreed fillies and the same number of colts, our last years crop. These fillies and colts are just similar to those you bought from us last year, being out of the same herd ... at our local show we were awarded four firsts, three second and three third prizes ...

Manufacturing
Acme Food and
ACME POULTRY FOOD
110 LA SALLE ST.
CHICAGO. 3/17/06.

In reply refer to File 2952

Messrs. Alexander Sandison & Sons,

Uyeasound, Shetland Islands.

Gentlemen;-

Wish to thank you very kindly for your favor of the 2nd inst., and am sorry to say that the present prices in this country will not permit of my paying 5L each for yearling fillies. The expense of importation is so very heavy that these ponies are a long ways from being cheap when they have reached Chicago.

Upon investigation, believe you gentlemen will find that I have purchased practically all the ponies that have left Shetland since last August, and believe that I have proven to be one of the largest dealers, and have bought more ponies in Shetland than have been purchased from that Island in this country in the last twenty-five or thirty years altogether, and if the prices are advancing there, you will all be obliged to give me the credit for it.

If at some time in the future you have some further ponies to offer, which you feel would interest me, I would indeed be much pleased to hear from you.

I was also very much pleased to learn of your success at the Pony Show, and trust your success in that regard will continue from year to year.

Please give my regards to all the Sandisons I have had the pleasure of meeting, and with best wishes, I remain,

Yours very truly,

GHS/R

Thomas A. and Franklin D. Simons,

Real Estate and Investments,

Room 61 Wheeler Building.

Columbus, Ohio. Mch 19th 1907.

Messrs A. Sandison & Sons,

　　　　Uyeasound, Shetland Islands.

Gentlemen:,

　　　　I want to buy some Shetland ponies and have been
referred to you.　Please state what you can sell me ponies
for of the following description:

　　　　First- One year old mares, perfectly sound, colors
black and bay.

　　　　Second- Two year old mares, sound, same colors,
bred and unbred.

　　　　Third- Three year old mares, sound, same colors,
bred and unbred.

　　　　Fourth- One stallion, entirely black, 35 to 40
inches high, 3 to 5 years old, of fine style, good action,
good breeder, and in every way a desirable head for a herd.

　　　　I want mares also of good form and such as will
not run over 42 inches.　State how many you have for sale.
If you cannot furnish them, kindly give me the name and
address of some one who can, and oblige,

　　　　　　　　Yours truly,

　　　　　　　　Thomas A. Simons

84

E.M.POSTON,President.
F.K.PENDLETON, V.Pres.& Genl. Counsel.
25 Broad St. New York.

H.G.MEREDITH, Vice President.
Detroit, Mich.
C.W.THOMPSON, Sec'y-Treas.

NEW YORK COAL COMPANY,

MINERS AND SHIPPERS

HOCKING VALLEY COAL.

COLUMBUS,OHIO.

BELL PHONE, 54.
INDEPENDENT PHONE, 646.

July 11, 1907.

Messrs. Alexander Sandison & Sons,

Baltasound, Shetland Islands,

Scotland,

Gentlemen:

Referring to our correspondence of October, 1905, we beg
to advise you that our agent, Mr. O. S. Pedrow, will be in the
Shetland Islands during the latter part of August and thr first of
September, this year, with the intention of buying some Shetland
Ponies. He will undoubtedly call upon you and other exporters of
ponies with this purpose in view. We send him as our duly accredited
representative, and would say that he is thoroughly responsible and
trustworthy, and has our full authority for any purchases he may make.

Thanking you in advance for any courtesies you may extend to him,
we beg to remain,

Yours truly,

President N. Y. Coal Company.

December 1907. From A. Sandison and Sons to Bartlett, U. S. A.:
... having already sold all that we have to dispose of this season (over a
hundred ponies) we regret that we have no pedigreed mares which we could
offer at present. However we shall have a nice lot of fillies for sale
(pedigreed) in the autumn of 1908 at £8 F.O.B. steamer here.

January 1908. From A. Sandison and Sons to Mrs Huband:
We sold our pedigreed mares much too freely at the beginning of the present
American demand and now we are having weekly, fresh enquiries from the
States and Canada for mares and have none to offer.

1908. To Guy Underwood, Ohio:
We have at different times sold a good many ponies to Americans, including Dr Elliott, the Simpsons of Chicago, Powell Brothers and others.

November 1908. To A. A. Ferguson, Delaware, Ohio, offering:
... twenty named ponies (all young) for £250 ... have sold 38 ponies to the U.S.A. from our Stud in the past three weeks.

FANTASTIC FACTS

An American who saw the start of Shetland pony popularity was Harry Cooper of Illinois, born in 1885, and still breeding Shetlands into the 1950s. His first mare was "Minnie Bruce" (72) imported from Shetland by John Bergen. As "Minnie Bruce" was unloaded from the train John Bergen was offered $500,00 for her, a tremendous price at that time, being the equivalent of £100.

Will Williams was an American fanatic from an early age and was in touch with the early importers. He bought his first Shetland in 1903 and his first stallion "Sensation" in 1905 from the J. M. Hoag stud. After Williams had used "Sensation" for several years he traded him for 640 acres of land in Texas. As this particular area was later developed as a gas and oil field "Sensation" (4270) probably bears the distinction of being the most profitable Shetland ever.

More recently, and nearer home, a handsome black filly foal was bought at the Unst Sale for one guinea. A few years later "Sylvanus" was exported to Norway where she was shown with great success, obtaining the highest accolade given there. She received this on the following merits: Feminine, typical of the breed, fine head, strong overline and good movement. She is now valued at a handsome three thousand pounds.

"Sylvanus" (should have been called Cinderella) – the one guinea foal.

CHAPTER TEN

THE SHETLAND PONY
STUD BOOK SOCIETY

We are fortunate that, in 1890, people had the foresight and enthusiasm to start a Stud Book for Shetland Ponies. Alexander Sandison was one of the founder members and, as such, received the early communications. I have included those that might be of interest to readers.

1988. From George Bruce, Seed Warehouse, 35 Market Street, Aberdeen:
Dear Sir,
    I am always doing something about "Shetland Stud Book" and have got the names of a good many good men willing to work. When can I call my friends to meet ?

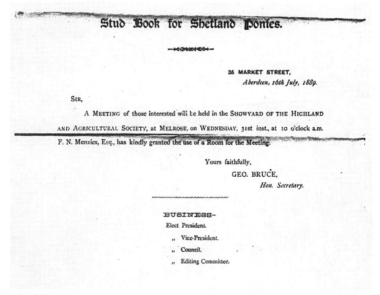

Stud Book for Shetland Ponies.

—————

35 MARKET STREET,
Aberdeen, 16th July, 1889.

SIR,

    A MEETING of those interested will be held in the SHOWYARD OF THE HIGHLAND

AND AGRICULTURAL SOCIETY, at MELROSE, on WEDNESDAY, 31st inst., at 10 o'clock a.m.

F. N. Menzies, Esq., has kindly granted the use of a Room for the Meeting.

Yours faithfully,
GEO. BRUCE,
Hon. Secretary.

BUSINESS—
Elect President.
  ,,   Vice-President.
  ,,   Council.
  ,,   Editing Committee.

An important step.

This list accompanied the notice of meeting.

Lord LONDONDERRY.

Lord ARTHUR CECIL.

ALLAN R. MACKENZIE, Yr. of Kintail.

A. I. FORTESCUE of Kingcausie.

CAMPBELL MACPHERSON GRANT of Drumduan.

GAVIN HADDEN of Dalmuinzie.

D. INGLIS of Flemington. *(Kergord - Shetland)*

JOHN ANDERSON, Hillswick.

JOHN BRUCE, Sumburgh, Shetland.

JOHN CHALMERS, Vensgarth. *(Tingwall)*

JOHN CRAIGIE, Ordal, Shetland.

ALEXANDER DAVIDSON of Uya Sound, Shetland.

JAMES DUNCAN, Fern Villa, Inverness.

GANSON BROTHERS, Lerwick.

RANALD MACDONALD, Cluny Estates Office.

ANDERSON MANSON, Laxfirth.

J. R. MEICKLEJOHN, Maryfield House.

W. S. PENNIE, Uyaf, Shetland.

A. SANDISON, Uya Sound, Shetland.

Rev. WILLIAM SMITH, Manse of Alush, Shetland.

November 1890. From George Bruce:
... I am glad to say that to all appearances owing to "Stud Book" prices are getting higher and demand increases.

35 MARKET STREET,

ABERDEEN, 2nd June, 1890.

SIR,

By this post I send you *draft* copy of the Rules and Bye-Laws of the proposed Stud Book for Shetland Ponies, and also draft copies of Entry Forms.

The question of *height* has not been settled, as many consider it unnecessary, but I will be glad to have your views on this subject, as well as any other suggestions you may think about.

By minute in Appendix, the breeders in Shetland have to elect representatives to consult and advise the Editing Committee. I hope, therefore, that you will lose no time in getting this done, as the Editing Committee meet at a very early date to finally arrange matters for Annual Meeting.

Yours faithfully,

George Bruce

HON. SECRETARY.

A. Sandison Esq
Uya Sound
Shetland

"The question of height has not been settled". Sounds familiar.

89

1889. From Alexander Sandison to George Bruce:

... As to height for Stud Book I fancy you will have to take up to 40 inches but I should prefer 39 in. only that would leave out many good real Shetlanders. I think 40 inches should not be exceeded.

December 1890. From George Bruce:

I hope you will manage to get as many breeders as possible in your neighbourhood to join the Society and enter their stock, to ensure the Society being a perfect success ...

1890. From Alexander Sandison to John Anderson, Hillswick:

... I think it right that we should have a meeting in Lerwick to consider the rules of the "Shetland Pony Stud Book".

April 1891. From Gavin Hadden:

... 6, 3yr old stallions [£21 at Lerwick] ... The prices are above my mark.

Lord Londonderry only got an average of a little over £27 for his horse ponies at Seaham harbour last week ... corn fed and fat; besides this many of them were over 3 years old and had pedigrees.

1891. From H. A. Rooke, Liverpool Block Works Ltd:

... 6 of the best you can pick out, black, brown or bay. Height to be as small as possible – not to exceed 39 in when fully grown. To be high in withers or shoulder and to have small heads. They must not be cow hocked and must be free from faults and have good style and action. They must not have their ears clipped and must be already in the Stud Book.

In fact I want really good ponies the style of "Tom Thumb" is the kind. I am getting a nice Stud about me and intend devoting both time and money showing them at local and other Shows in England and trying to get classes formed where they don't already exist, all of which will help a little to keep up the name of the "Shelties". You will therefore see I want nothing but the best or else my efforts will be in vain.

Further on 8th May after nine letters:

... The pony has arrived well. I am very pleased with it.

1890. From James Duncan.

... particulars that might be useful for Pony Stud Book or the grey or drab coloured pony I had from you 2 years ago. I think you bought it from a neighbour ...

Note below – June and Prince.

1891. From Rev. C. E. Barnes:

... 2 Shetland mares not likely to be over 39 inches, one a chestnut (light with silver points if possible) the other cream or piebald ... having looked through the Shetland Stud Book you seem to be the only breeder in possession of these colours. The produce of the following if height is right, seems to be what I want, 350, 352, 255 and 362.

Is "Nestor" for sale.

1890. From Alexander Sandison to Mr Paton:
... Shetland ponies have gone up in price in the last 12 months more than
they have done for years past ... We have over 100 entries in the Stud Book.
We have half a dozen specially selected stallions coming three years and a
fine lot of mares rising two years.

THE

Shetland Pony Stud-Book

SOCIETY.

35 MARKET STREET,

ABERDEEN, *3 July* 189 *1*

DEAR SIR,

I am directed to inform you that, in accord-
ance with your request, you were, at a Meeting of the
Council held to-day, admitted a *Life*
Member of the Society.

The first contribution of £ *7:17:6* *has been paid* to the
Funds of the Society ~~is now due. Kindly remit at~~
~~early convenience.~~

Your obedient Servant,

George Bruce

SECRETARY.

Alex Sandison Esq
Uyasound

Life membership granted.

91

DAILUAINE– GLENLIVET DISTILLERY, LTD.
CARRON– STRATHSPEY, N.B.

22nd August 1893

Alexander Sandison Esq,
 Unasound,
Shetland.

Dear Sir,

Referring to your letter of 13th January 1891 to Hm. S mackay Esq. Egm.! We shall be glad to know if you have now entered your ponies in Stud Book, and if so how many of the ponies sold to Mr Henrison have been entered. –

Yours faithfully,

DAILUAINE-GLENLIVET DISTILLERY, LTD.,
Thos Mackenzie DIRECTOR.

P.S. The ponies are our property. We may require some more shortly. T.D.S. C.u.

There were many similar queries.

Telegraph Address:-
BRYDON, SEAHAM-HARBOUR.

Memorandum

FROM

Robert Brydon.

Londonderry Estates Office.

Seaham Harbour. 17. 11 1893

To Messrs Sandison, Uya Sound —
Shetland

Gentlemen,

I bought some Ponies from Mr Mackenzie, Carronstrathspey which it seems he procured from you. Three of these, all Blacks; each 5 yrs old, 2 10 hands + 1 10.2 have been sold to a gentleman who wishes to register them, Can you help me in getting this done? If you can I shall be much obliged, I think all the information that is wanted is the name of the Breeder.

Believe me
Yours faithfully
R Brydon

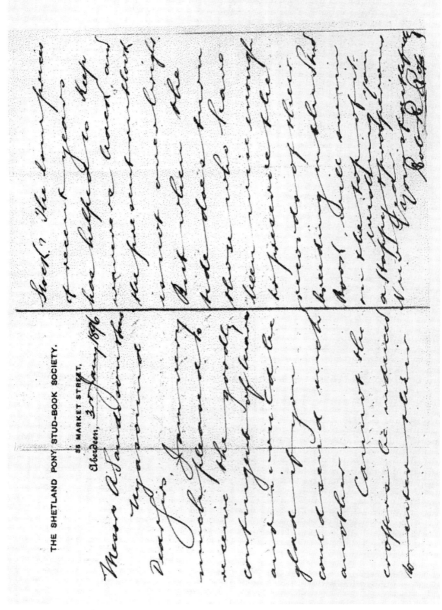

Wise words from the secretary.

THE SHETLAND PONY STUD-BOOK SOCIETY.

ROBT. R. ROSS,
SECRETARY.

BALMORAL BUILDINGS, 67 GREEN,

Aberdeen, ... 23rd May, 1905 ....

Messrs A. Sandison & Sons,
            Uyasound,
                        Shetland.

Dear Sirs,

      I am sending your Circular with reference to advertising Registered Ponies for Sale by same post, and I will be glad if you will send me Entries for same for first issue which takes place as you will see on Ist July. The List of those for sale will be advertised in a number of the principal South papers, and you should have a favourable opportunity through this list of getting into touch with the best buyers. I am disappointed to have no Entries from you for Volume XV. and as this Volume is now ready to go to press, I would be glad if you could send me your Entries by return of post, as it would be very disappointing to miss your Entries after all those years you have contributed so much to the success of the Society.

                      I am,

                         Yours faithfully,

Early advertising.

SHETLAND PONY CIRCULAR.

The following SHETLAND PONIES are advertised for Sale.

They are all entered in the Shetland Pony Stud-Book, and are therefore pure-bred Ponies. The entry in the Stud-Book states their age and pedigree so far as known.

Intending Purchasers should communicate direct, in every case, with the Advertiser, and not with the Secretary of the Stud-Book Society, who cannot undertake to give advice or otherwise to take part in any transaction.

Dr. J. C. BOWIE, Clousta, by Bixter, Shetland, N.B.

"**BERSERKER**" (286), Stallion, Black, 5 years, 37 inches, good stock-getter, foals almost always black colour. When two-year-old, received H.C. at Lerwick Show.

WILLIAM CHAPMAN, Agnew Villa, Helensburgh.

I.—"**NORRIE**" (1281), Mare, Black, foaled 1895, 36 inches. Sire, "Oman" (33); dam, "Niobe" (1007), by "Odin" (32).
> With Filly Foal at Foot, by "Naughty" (204).

II.—"**DANEGELT**," Entire Colt, Brown, foaled 1902, 34 inches. Sire, "Vengeance" (263); dam, "Danish Queen" (1424); grand sire, "Emeer" (131), by "Vesta" (215); great grand sire, "Odin" (32), by "Dinah" (525). Beautiful Pony; should sire small stock.

III.—"**TRUMP**," Entire Colt, Black, foaled 1903. Sire, "Harold" (117); dam, "Thyra" (1499), by "Vespa" (166). Most promising young Stallion, with quality and all-round action.

CHARLES DOUGLAS, Auchlochan, Lesmahagow, Lanarkshire.

I.—"**BEATRICE III.**," (1648), Mare, Black, 7 years old, 38 inches high. Stylish Mare, good action. Served by "Duncan" (147).

II.—"**PRIMROSE**" (1375), Mare, Black, 10 years old, 38 inches high. Handsome Pony, quiet in harness, good breeder. Served by "Frederick" (223).

III.—"**PHLOX**," Filly Foal of "Primrose" (1375), by "Duncan" (147). Promising Foal.

Mrs. FOX, Outhill, Studley, Warwickshire.

"**LIGHTNING**" (Vol. XIV., page 17), Two-year-old Skewbald Colt, by "Magician" (154); dam, "Moonlight" (469). This is a very good-looking Colt, 37 inches high. He has a beautiful fore-end and good bone.

WILLIAM MUNGALL, Transy, Dunfermline.

"**STELLIO**" (Vol. XIV., page 73), Colt, Black, foaled 25th April, 1903. Dam, "Stella" (1692); sire, "Hector" (183).

"**SILVER KING**" (Vol. XV., page 40), Colt, Black, foaled 4th May, 1904. Dam, "Silver Queen" (1197); sire, "Hector" (183). The Dams and Sire of these Colts are well-known Winners.

The Shetland Pony Stud-Book Society, Balmoral Buildings, 67-71 Green, Aberdeen.

ROBERT R. ROSS, Secretary.

A few took advantage of the opportunity.

June 1906. To R. R. Ross Shetland Pony Stud Book Society:
... We are extremely sorry to learn that you are giving up the secretaryship
for we have always felt that it was largely through you that the Stud Book
Society has been a success in the past.

November 1907. From Thomas Sandison to the Secretary to the Shetland Pony
Stud Book Society:
... Regarding the resolution of the Council not to publish prizes taken at the
Unst Agricultural Show, we must say we are surprised to learn that such a
resolution has been passed, and we think it wrong that a Show like that of
the Unst Agricultural Society, where a large number of excellent ponies are
exhibited should be black-listed. There are only two Shows in the County, the
'Shetland' which serves the mainland division and the 'Unst' which serves
the North Isles division, and owing to the detached and insular position, both
Shows are necessary, and to admit Lerwick and exclude Unst is, we consider,
both unjust and unwise. We cannot see how publishing prizes won at the
Unst Show could in any way lead to confusion and we protest against the
action of the Council and hope you may lay the matter before the next
meeting and that you may be authorised to publish lists in the forthcoming
Volume.

December 1908. The following letter was written in response to the proposal to
form the Shetland Islands Stud book. Thomas Sandison was councillor for North
Yell at the time. To Mr D. Sinclair, Greenbank, North Yell:
Dear Sir,
    I received your letter of the 9th inst, enclosing petition re. the proposal to
form a Shetland Pony Stud-Book to be controlled by the County Council,
yesterday morning after the steamer had sailed so that I had no chance to
forward it by the "Earl". I am sending the petition to the County Clerk and
asking him to lay it before the council at their next meeting.
    I would be strongly in favour of anything that would be likely to help the
crofters in finding a ready sale for their ponies at the best prices possible. But
I think the sort of Stud Book proposed would be utterly valueless. The
County Council could not legally take any responsibility for a Stud Book, but
even granting that it could be established, and that it would be recognised by
buyers, it would be many years before crofters could have a pony with a
pedigree long enough to be eligible for export to the U. S. A.
    It would be much better for the County Council and the Parish Councils
throughout the Islands to petition the Council of the Shetland Pony Stud-
Book Society to open the Stud Book for, say, a year to enable all crofters
having ponies to have an opportunity of entering them.
                            Yours truly,
                            Thos. A. Sandison.

In fact, four Shetland Islands Stud Books were printed largely at the instigation
of Peter Anderson, a dealer who had quarrelled with the S.P.S.B.S. but they proved
to be valueless as Thomas Sandison predicted, especially as they were not accepted
by the American authorities.

PERTH AUCTION MARKET.

PERTH weekly sales of store & dairy stock on FRIDAYS & of fat stock on MONDAYS.

J.M. FRASER.
MANAGING DIRECTOR.

FORTNIGHTLY sales of horses held on MONDAYS.
GLASGOW weekly sales of fat & dairy stock held every WEDNESDAY.
INVERNESS weekly sales of fat, store, and dairy stock on MONDAYS.
DUNFERMLINE weekly sales of fat and store stock held every TUESDAY.
THORNTON weekly sales of fat, store, and dairy stock every MONDAY.
and monthly sales of horses on MONDAY.
STIRLING weekly sales of fat, store, and dairy stock every THURSDAY.
SALES OF WOOL HELD PERIODICALLY AT PERTH AS ADVERTISED.
Ample Keep and Accommodation for all kinds of Stock previous to and after Sale.

TELEGRAPHIC ADDRESS.
"FRASER, PERTH."   TELEPHONE Nº II.

PERTH, 28th Oct. 190 2

Messrs Alexander Sandison & Sons,

Uyasound,

Shetland.

Dear Sirs,

We have pleasure in enclosing herewith catalogue of pedigree
Shetland ponies belonging to the Marchioness of Linlithgow (Lady Hopetoun) which we are to sell here on Monday next, 3rd November. We
shall be much pleased to see you present at the sale, and are,

Yours faithfully,

For Macdonald, Fraser, & Co, Ltd.

An interesting catalogue follows.

OF

Pedigree Shetland Ponies

The Property of the Marchioness of Linlithgow

(Lady HOPETOUN),

At Perth Auction Market, Perth

On MONDAY Next, 3rd November. 1902

MACDONALD, FRASER, & CO., Ltd., honoured with instructions from the Marchioness of LINLITHGOW, will submit to Public Auction as above—

15 High-Class Pedigree Shetland Ponies,

as follows :—

BROOD MARES.

1   "MOONLIGHT" (469).

Sire—"GIANT" (10).   Dam—"COQUETTE" (103).

Foaled 1888. Bay, 35¾ in. high. She has wonderful bone, and is a perfect type of Shetland Pony. Gained first prize at R.N.A.S. Show, Aberdeen, 1891. Served by "Magician."

"EVA" (118).

Sire—"YOUNG VISCOUNT" (48).   Dam—"ERICA" (783).

Foaled 1893. 37½ in. high.   A beautiful pony.   Served by
" Magician." (154 S. P. S. Bh.)

---

3   "GUINEA PIG" (974).

Sire—"MULTUM IN PARVO" (28).   Dam—"TWILIGHT" (471).

Foaled 1891. Skewbald. 37½ inches.   A beautiful pony.
She has been served by "Multum in Parvo"

---

4   "THEO."

Sire—"DOUGLAS" (145).   Dam—"THORLINDE" (1263).

Foaled 1898. Black. 36 inches.   A beautiful pony.
Served by " Multum in Parvo."

---

5   "MARGUERITE" (1262).

Sire—"MONSTER" (133).   Dam—"MARGERINE" (490).

Foaled, April 15th, 1895. Bay. 37¼ in.   Served by "Douglas"
(145).

Note.—" Marguerite " is the dam of " Dulcemona " who gained
first prize at H. & A. Show, Stirling, July, 1900.

6   "GLORIA."

Sire—"DOUGLAS" (145).   Dam—"GUINEA PIG (974).

Foaled, 1900. Brown.   Very small   Has been served by "Magician."

FOALS.

7   COLT, foaled April 1st, 1902.

Sire—"DOGLAS" (145)   Dam—"MARGUERITE" (1262).

---

8   COLT, foaled April 19th, 1902.

Sire—"MAGICIAN" (154).   Dam—"MOONLIGHT" (469).

---

9   FILLY foal, foaled May 30th, 1902.

Sire—"MAGICIAN" (154).   Dam—"GUINEA PIG" (974).

---

10   FILLY, foaled May 18th, 1902.

Sire—"MULTUM IN PARVO" (28).   Dam—"THEO" (1515).

---

11   COLT, foaled May, 1902.

Sire—"DOUGLAS" (145).   Dam—"MARGOT."

12   FILLY, foaled May 6th, 1902.

Sire—" MULTUM IN PARVO " (28).   Dam—"FREESIA."

---

13   COLT, foaled May 11th, 1902.

Sire—" DOUGLAS " (145).   Dam—" STARLIGHT."

---

14   FILLY, foaled April 16th, 1902.

Sire—" MAGICIAN " (154).   Dam—" BANTAM " (1177).

---

15   COLT, foaled April 6th, 1902.

Sire—" DOUGLAS " (145).   Dam—" MOMENTO " (1514).

BREED DESCRIPTION

Height: Registered stock must not exceed 40 inches (102cms) at three years or under, nor 42 inches (107cms) at four years or over. Ponies are measured from the withers to the ground, by measuring stick, and a level stance, preferably concrete should be used.

Colour: Shetland ponies may be any colour known in horses except spotted.

Coat: The coat changes according to the seasons: a double coat in winter with guard hairs which shed the rain and keep the pony's skin completely dry in the

A group of ponies about 100 years ago at Cruister. "Well placed" forelegs and "pleny of heart room".   © *Shetland Museum*

worst of the weather and, by contrast, a short summer coat which should carry a beautiful silky sheen. At all times the mane and tail hair should be long, straight and profuse and the feathering of the fetlocks straight and silky.

Head: The head should be small, carried well and in proportion. Ears should be small and erect, wide set but pointing well forward. Forehead should be broad with bold, dark, intelligent eyes. Muzzle must be broad with nostrils wide and open. Teeth and jaw must be correct.

Forelegs: Should be well-placed with sufficient good, flat bone. Strong forearm. Short balanced cannon bone. Springy pasterns.

Hindlegs: The thighs should be strong and muscular with well-shaped strong hocks, neither hooky nor too straight. When viewed from behind, the hindlegs should not be set too widely apart, nor should the hocks be turned in.

Feet: Tough, round and well-shaped - not too short, narrow, contracted or thin.

Body: The neck should be properly set onto the shoulder, which in turn should be sloping, not upright, and end in a well defined wither. The body should be strong, with plenty of heart room, well-sprung ribs, the loin strong and muscular. The quarters should be broad and long with tail set well up on them.

Action: Straight, free action using every joint. Tracking up well.

General: A most salient and essential feature of the Shetland pony is its general air of vitality (presence), stamina and robustness.

STALLIONS

The first 48 stallions registered in Stud Book I which includes many famous names.

STALLIONS.

VOLUME FIRST.

BEAMISH. (1)

Foaled about 1874.   Black.   38 inches.

Breeder unknown; property of J. Joicey & Co., Bushblades, Chester-le-street.

Purchased from Mr. Adie, Voe.

BLACK BEAUTY. (2)

Foaled 1885.   Black.   37 inches.

Bred by and property of John Bruce of Sumburgh, Lerwick. Sire, Black Prince (6); dam, Young Brownie (76), by a pure Shetland stallion; gr. dam, Old Brownie, by a pure Shetland stallion.

BLACK BOB. (3)

Foaled 1884.   Black.   40 inches.

Bred by Alexander Sandison, Uyasound, Shetland; property of Anderson Manson, Laxfirth, Lerwick.

BLACK CHIEF. (4)

Foaled 1885.   Black.   37½ inches.

Bred by Alexander Inkster, Reawick, Shetland; property of Thomas M. Adie, Voe, Shetland.

BLACK JACK. (5)

Foaled 1883.   Black.   38 inches.

Bred by Alexander Sandison, Uyasound, Shetland; property of Anderson Manson, Laxfirth, Lerwick.

105

BLACK PRINCE.   (6)
Foaled 1880.   Black.   37 inches.
Bred by and property of John Bruce of Sumburgh, Lerwick.
Sire, Rufus (37); dam, Fair Maid, by Wildboy.

BUNESS.   (7)
Foaled 1884.   Black.   42 inches.
Bred by and property of Mrs. Ursula Edmonston of Buness,
Baltasound, Shetland.   Sire, Balta.

Balta won 1st Prize at the Highland and Agricultural Society's Show at
Inverness in 1874.

CHARLIE.   (8)
Foaled   { Skewbald (red and }   42 inches.
May, 1883.   {   white).   }
Bred by and property of Widow Donald Tulloch, Braewick,
Hillswick, Shetland.

CORBIE.   (9)
Foaled 25 April, 1885.   Black.   38 inches.
Bred by the Marquis of Londonderry, Bressay, Shetland;
property of John Anderson & Sons, Hillswick, Shetland.
Sire, Lord of the Isles (26); dam, Kate, by Lion 2nd (23);
gr. dam, Katherine, by Tom Thumb (44); 3 dam, Kirsty, by
Jack (16).

GIANT.   (10)
            { Bay, with four white }
Foaled 1883. { legs, and white spot }   35½ inches.
            { on near shoulder.   }
Bred by the Marquis of Londonderry, B-essay, Shetland;
property of the Countess of Hopetoun, Hopetoun House,
South Queensferry. Sire, Jack (16); dam, a piebald mare,
one of Lord Londonderry's original stock.

GLADSTONE. (11)

Foaled 1885.   Dark brown.   38½ inches.

Bred by and property of Alexander Sandison, Uyasound, Unst, Shetland.

HAEGARIE. (12)

Foaled 1884.   Black.   40 inches.

Breeder unknown ; property of John Anderson & Sons, Hillswick, Shetland.

HAMNAVOE. (13)

Foaled about 1876.   Blue, roan, and white.   39 inches.

Breeder unknown ; property of John Harrison, Hamnavoe, Hillswick, Shetland.

HOLMSIDE. (14)

Foaled 1878.   Brown.   42 inches.

Breeder unknown ; property of Hedley Brothers, Holmside Hall, Chester-le-street.

Holmside (14) at one time belonged to James Lindsley, Durham, who bought him from Anderson Manson, Laxfirth, Lerwick.

IVANHOE. (15)

Foaled 1878.   Grey.   41 inches.

Bred by John Anderson, Hillswick, Shetland ; property of Peter Manson, Lunna, Voe, Shetland.

JACK. (16)

Foaled 1871.   Black.   40 inches.

Breeder unknown ; property of the Marquis of Londonderry, Bressay, Shetland.

Jack (16) is sire of Lord of the Isles (26), Laird of Noss (20), Odin (32), Darling (174), Sprightly, &c.

SHETLAND PONY STUD-BOOK.

JACK. (17)

Foaled September, 1883.   Black.   42 inches.

Bred by and property of Jacob Anderson, Brae Houlland, Hillswick, Shetland.

JACK III. (18)

Foaled May, 1883.   Deep black.   42 inches.

Bred by and property of Sinclair Pottinger, Grimasta, Lerwick. Sire, Jack II.; dam, Gipsy.

Jack I., grandsire of Jack III., when 3 years old—in 1867—gained at Lerwick the Earl of Zetland's 1st Prize for Pure Stallion 3 to 6 years old; the Aberdeen, Leith, and Clyde Shipping Company's 1st Prize; and the Shetland Agricultural Society's 1st Prize for Best Stallion of any age.

JILL. (19)

Foaled 1864.   Black.   36 inches.

Breeder unknown; property of the Countess of Hopetoun, Hopetoun House, South Queensferry.

Was brought direct from Shetland by the late Mr. Wylie of Woodcockdale, Linlithgowshire.

Gained Gold Medal in 1871 at the Royal Agricultural Society's Show at Islington, and 1st Prize in 1885 at the West Lothian Show at Linlithgow.

LAIRD OF NOSS. (20)

Foaled 5 May, 1880.   { Black, white spot on rib }   38 inches.

Bred by and property of the Marquis of Londonderry, Bressay, Shetland. Sire, Jack (16); dam, Seivwright, by Lofty.

LINTIE. (21)

Foaled June, 1885.   Brown.   37½ inches.

Bred by John Henderson, Sandwick, Unst, Shetland; property of John Anderson & Sons, Hillswick, Shetland.

LION. (22)

Foaled 1864. Dun. 36 inches.

Bred by John Bruce of Sumburgh, Shetland ; property of the
Marquis of Londonderry, Bressay, Shetland.

LION II. (23)

Foaled 1880. Dun. 36 inches.

Bred by and property of the Marquis of Londonderry, Bressay,
Shetland. Sire, Lion (22) ; dam, Mitchell.

LITTLE DUKE. (24)

Foaled 1883. Bay. 40 inches.

Breeder unknown ; property of W. W. F. Osborne, 19 Stanbury
Road, Peckham, London, S.E.

Purchased by Mr. Osborne in the Island of Unst, in 1886.

LITTLE VIKING. (25)

Foaled 1870. Bay, black points. $35\frac{1}{2}$ inches.

Bred by the late Joseph Leask of Sand, Lerwick ; property of
James Duncan, Fern Villa, Inverness.

Gained three 1st Prizes at Glasgow Stallion Show.

LORD OF THE ISLES. (26)

Foaled 16 May, 1875. Black. 36 inches.

Bred by and property of the Marquis of Londonderry, Bressay,
Shetland. Sire, Jack (16) ; dam, Dandy.

Gained at the Highland and Agricultural Society's Shows the following
prizes :—Medal at Edinburgh, 1884; 1st Prize at Aberdeen, 1885; 1st Prize at
Melrose, 1889.

MARQUIS. (27)

Foaled 1884. Black. 38 inches.

Bred by the Marquis of Londonderry, Bressay, Shetland ; property of Andrew M'Farlane, Kingussie. Sire, Lord of the
Isles (26).

Gained 2nd Prize at the Highland and Agricultural Society's Show at
Dundee, 1890.

MULTUM IN PARVO.   (28)

Foaled 1884.   Brown.   37 inches.

Bred by the Marquis of Londonderry, Bressay, Shetland; property of Gavin Hadden of Dalmuinzie, Murtle, Aberdeen. Sire, Lord of the Isles (26); dam, Dandy, by Prince of Thule (36).

Gained at the Highland and Agricultural Society's Shows these prizes:— 2nd Prize at Melrose, 1889, and 3rd Prize at Dundee, 1890.

NESTOR.   (29)

Foaled May, 1880.   Bay, black points.   39½ inches.

Bred by and property of Alexander Sandison, Uyasound, Unst, Shetland. Sire, Blackie; dam, Portia (356).

NORIE.   (30)

Foaled 1881.   Brown, black points.   42 inches.

Breeder unknown; property of John Anderson & Sons, Hillswick, Shetland.

Purchased from James Hay, Burravoe, Yell, who bought him when a foal in Unst.

NORSEMAN.   (31)

Foaled May, 1883.   Black.   39½ inches.

Bred by and property of Alexander Sandison, Uyasound, Unst, Shetland. Sire, Blackie; dam, Minna, by Brownie; gr. dam, Lady Gray.

ODIN.   (32)

Foaled 12 May, 1880.   Black.   38 inches.

Bred by and property of the Marquis of Londonderry, Bressay, Shetland. Sire, Jack (16); dam, Nugget, by Tom Thumb (44).

Gained 1st Prize at the Highland and Agricultural Society's Show at Dumfries, 1886—only time shown.

O M A N. (33)

Foaled 5 May, 1885.   Brown.   34 inches.

Bred by and property of the Marquis of Londonderry, Bressay, Shetland. Sire, Prince of Thule (36); dam, Norna, by Lord of the Isles (26).

Gained 2nd Prize at the Highland and Agricultural Society's Show in Glasgow, 1888.

O S C A R. (34)

Foaled 1883.   Black.   39½ inches.

Bred by John Craigie, Ordale, Baltasound, Shetland; property of Ranald Macdonald, Ormiclate Farm, South Uist. Sire, Albert.

Albert was a grand pony. Exported to South America, and sold there for £200.

PRINCE OF HOULLAND. (35)

Foaled 1881.   Piebald (black and white).   41 inches.

Bred by Andrew Johnson, Suster, Voe, Shetland : property of Thomas Thomason, Priest Houlland, Hillswick, Shetland.

PRINCE OF THULE. (36)

Foaled 1872.   Brown.   36 inches.

Breeder unknown ; property of the Marquis of Londonderry, Bressay, Shetland.

Gained 2nd Prize at the Highland and Agricultural Society's Show at Aberdeen, 1885, when shown against Lord of the Isles (26)—the only time shown.

Sire of Oman (33), Vane Tempest (47), Paris, Princess, Vesta, &c.

Purchased from John Walker, Bressay.

R U F U S. (37)

Foaled 1873.   Red.   37 inches.

Bred by and property of John Bruce of Sumburgh, Shetland. Sire, Grey Hillswick ; dam, Fair Islander, by a pure Shetland stallion.

SAMPSON.   (38)

Foaled 1883.   Brown.   38 inches.

Bred by and property of John Bruce of Sumburgh, Shetland.
Sire, Rufus (37); dam, Kitty, by Wildboy.; gr. dam, Red
Rose, by a pure Shetland stallion.

SAXFORD.   (39)

Foaled 1885.   Brown.   39 inches.

Breeder unknown; property of the Marquis of Londonderry,
Bressay, Shetland.

Purchased from Simon Anderson, Setter, Bressay.

SCORIE.   (40)

Foaled May, 1885. Bay, with black points.   41¾ inches.

Bred by David Robertson, Burravoe, Lerwick; property of John
Anderson & Sons, Hillswick, Shetland. Sire, Norie (30).

SIR HENRY.   (41)

Foaled 1883.   Bay, with black points.   41 inches.

Bred by Alexander Scott, Noss House, Wick; property of
James Duncan, Fern Villa, Inverness. Sire, Rattler; dam,
Beauty.

Gained two 1st Prizes at the Royal Northern Agricultural Society's Show at
Aberdeen, and several 1st Prizes at the Farmers' Society's Shows at Inverness.

SPARROW.   (42)

Foaled 1883.   Brown.   41 inches.

Breeder unknown; property of John Anderson & Sons, Hillswick, Shetland.

THE MARQUIS.   (43)

Foaled 1883.   Strawberry roan.   41 inches.

Bred by the Marquis of Londonderry, Bressay, Shetland; property of W. W. F. Osborne, 19 Stanbury Road, Peckham,
London, S.E. Sire, Jack (16).

TOM THUMB. (44)

Foaled 1864.   Black.   34 inches.

Breeder unknown; property of the Marquis of Londonderry, Bressay, Shetland.

Sire of Katherine, Jip, Quirky, Nugget, Gymer, Urd, &c.

TRIPTOLEMUS. (45)

Foaled May, 1882. Bay, with black points. $39\frac{1}{4}$ inches.

Bred by James Jaffray, Belmont, Lerwick; property of Alexander Sandison, Uyasound, Unst, Shetland. Sire, Blackie (belonging to A. Sandison); dam, Groga.

TYSTIE. (46)

Foaled 1882.   Black.   41 inches.

Breeder unknown: property of John Anderson & Sons, Hillswick, Shetland.

Purchased from Alexander Sandison, Uyasound, Unst.

VANE TEMPEST. (47)

Foaled 1882.   Bay.   38 inches.

Bred by the Marquis of Londonderry, Bressay, Shetland; property of John Bruce of Sumburgh, Shetland. Sire, Prince of Thule (36); dam, Kate (192), by Lion (22); gr. dam, Katharine, by Tom Thumb (44); 3 dam, Kirsty, by Jack (16).

YOUNG VISCOUNT. (48)

Foaled 1883.   Black.   37 inches.

Bred by the Marquis of Londonderry, Bressay, Shetland; property of Campbell Macpherson-Grant of Drumduan, Forres. Sire, Lord of the Isles (26).

No. 15 of Lord Londonderry's Catalogue in 1889.

CHAPTER ELEVEN

STALLIONS SCHEMES

NATURAL SELECTION

It must be remembered that until the middle of the 19th century there were no fences in Shetland and only the few farms that existed would have had fields enclosed by proper drystone dykes. As far as the crofters were concerned only the hill "dyke", the drystone wall between the crofts and the common or "scattald" was stock proof.

The ponies spent most of their lives on the scattald and although they were all "owned" they were running wild as they had done for centuries and only caught when necessary to perform some chore. This situation, above all, was the making of the Shetland pony for under these conditions the ponies were subject to natural selection. Weakness in any form meant certain death, whether it was a weakness of movement, enough to hinder the pony to forage successfully, or a lack of winter coat to protect it from the elements. Foaling problems were naturally bred out. More importantly only the strongest stallions would have come to the fore to claim their herd of mares and pass on their all important genes. These stallions would only be replaced when some young stallion was strong and forceful enough to challenge and fight for the chosen position. Whether it be a rutt of stags in the Highlands or a fight to the death in the Masai Mara the basic principles still apply.

In this situation superiority of size does not always guarantee success. I

Running wild as they should.   © *Dennis Coutts*

114

remember watching "Fireball of Marshwood" keeping his mares in order on the hill at Belmont. He may have been only 33½ inches but as he streaked along the hillside he was every inch a stallion and prepared to take on the world if need be.

Many years ago when the vast Walls and Sandness scattald was "cleared out" an old stallion was found, a stylish old fellow with many battle scars. He had fought and finally lost his battle for supremacy.

The first event to upset this natural selection was the demand from the coal mines. Only the males from four years to twelve years were sought after and while it was splendid to find an outlet for males it was overdone as dealer after dealer took their pick of the strongest and best. Alexander Sandison speaks of four dealers buying ponies in Unst in one week. Potential stallions were being lost to the breed as the numbers of ponies in the islands plummeted.

Even the estimated ten thousand ponies could not stand up to the constant demand. As these ponies were mostly on the scattald, it would seem that the hills were more productive then, than they are today, overgrazed, as they are, by the selective and ubiquitous sheep. We know from the Statistical Account of the 1790s that there was only a fraction of today's sheep numbers.

Further pressure on the numbers of island ponies came at the end of the 19th century with the American demand for quality mares and the best stallions. They wanted the best and were prepared to pay for them. Alexander Sandison who had a definite breeding policy admits to selling mares too readily to America. It must have been more tempting for crofters, who were in dire straits, to sell a pony when they were offered a tempting price.

In 1865 it was noted that "few people have any idea of the extent of the Shetland Pony trade." One noted dealer bought over in one season 1857 no fewer than 400. In 1861, 600 went south by steamer and perhaps fifty more by sailing vessels.

In 1874 however the total number of Shetland ponies had reached a very low point as had all other types of livestock. Severe weather followed by crop failures in the 1870s may have caused this drop in livestock numbers. However, the following year a dramatic increase in the total number of ponies confirms that the breeding of Shetland ponies for export was underway.

THE FIRST STALLION SCHEME

Mercifully a few people realised the extent of the problem so, when the Congested Districts Scotland Act was passed in 1897 to assist less favoured areas, a rudimentary stallion scheme was started. To begin with nine stallions were sent up from Scotland. Guardians kept the stallions and, for a small fee, anyone could bring a mare forward for service. The Board of Agriculture for Scotland took an interest and, in fact, took over the running of the scheme.

It must have proved reasonably successful for the number of stallions increased to twenty two at the beginning of the First World War when about six hundred mares were served. At this time the mares were used for flitting peats and so were used to being handled, an important factor in the success of the scheme. In 1932 the scheme was abandoned due to cuts by the Treasury. That last sentence has a familiar ring to it.

The First World War had a huge impact on the pony world. No more ponies were crossing the Atlantic and the home market almost dried up as shows ceased and pleasurable pursuits were forgotten. Cheaper ponies were imported for the mines so Shetland ponies were practically unsellable. This was particularly true of island ponies where the added freight was a burden. Registrations from 1914 dropped to one fifth over the next twenty years.

Well-known breeders and dealers went out of the pony business. Among these were A. Sandison and Sons and the Andersons of Hillswick.

THE PREMIUM STALLION SCHEME

The Department of Agriculture for Scotland resumed sending stallions to Shetland in the late forties but few people took advantage of this because the trade was so depressed. Mr James Dean who was Livestock Inspector for the D.O.A.S. invited Mr and Mrs Cox to accompany him to Shetland in 1948 and so began their lifelong involvement with the islands. That particular visit was to assess the impact the Department stallions were having on the breed and to inspect mares that had had foals to the stallions. This inspection scheme had been approved by the Council of the Shetland Pony Stud Book Society but on the whole the Council considered the island ponies beyond redemption.

Mrs Cox poses "Supremacy of Marshwood" with ease.

116

The following notice appeared in a *Farming News* (21ˢᵗ May 1948):
Livestock Inspector of the Department of Agriculture for Scotland is to visit Shetland at the end of this month for the purpose of selecting mares to be put to the stallions allocated under the Department's Shetland Pony Stallion Scheme. The Inspector will be in Unst on May 26ᵗʰ and 27ᵗʰ and in the Walls district on May 28ᵗʰ. Owners should at once notify Mr J. Smith, Berry, Scalloway and have mares ready for inspection.

The 1948 visit had a huge impact on the Coxes. They were shocked at the quality of a big percentage of the pony stock that they saw and began campaigning in Council and elsewhere for a Society run scheme. Mrs Cox could be a very forceful lady and the fact that she was Vice President and then President of the Society no doubt helped the cause. The Premium Stallion Scheme came into being in 1956 and the trials and tribulations that preceded it have been well covered in previous books.

The late Andrew Jamieson of Belmont at one of the first pony sales in Unst.

The island crofters were unaware of the resurrected American trade so the high prices at the first sale at Baltasound in 1957 came as a complete surprise. Over the next few years the market remained buoyant and the stallion scheme, which was largely funded by the Betting and Levy Board, was certainly a success. We owe a debt to the many mainland breeders who sent up decent, and in many cases, outstanding stallions to the islands. The following lists of Premium Stallions will be of interest to many and come courtesy of Myrna Flaws who has been secretary to the Pony Breeders of Shetland for many years. They managed the Premium

117

Stallion Scheme and later on the Premium Mare Scheme where a potential breeding mare is inspected for type and correctness at three years of age. This scheme was introduced to encourage breeders in Shetland to keep their best young mares for breeding.

The effects of the Stallion Scheme are apparent everywhere in the islands. In general the ponies have greatly improved and their heads in particular. The majority of breeders prior to the Premium Stallion Scheme had failed to register their stock because they would have been out of pocket to do so, so poor was the trade. After 1958, when the Society had arranged for the Inspection of mares with foal at foot, and the crofters realised there was a market for their foals, all that changed. The Coxes enthusiasm was infectious and their example at Gletness was watched with interest and appreciation. They were doing what the Marquis of Londonderry had done almost a century earlier by buying selected island ponies and close-breeding them.

Today, thanks to the Premium Stallion Scheme and the concentrated efforts of an enthusiastic few, there is in Shetland a core of dedicated breeders who are genuinely interested in the breed and it's future.

PREMIUM SCHEME STALLIONS
Unst
1956

CLIBBERSWICK	Wells Prince (1613) - Black - 37½"
	Sovereign of Marshwood (1609) - Skewbald - 39"
UNGERSTA	Littlestroke Neptune (1562) - White - 38"
ORDALE	Brian of Longhaugh (1533) - Black - 39"
UYEASOUND	Benvorlich (1553) - Piebald - 37"
COLVADALE	Spaniard of Marshwood (1484) - Black - 39½"
MUNESS	Blue Bonnet of Mundurno (1436) - Grey - 40½"

1957

CLIBBERSWICK	Donnachaidh Saigean (1645) - Black - 37"
UNGERSTA	Eckington Kirriemuir (1571) - Black
ORDALE	Sprinkle of Marshwood (1611) - Black - 40"
UYEASOUND	Polydor of Holne (1421) - White - 40"
COLVADALE	Robin (1607) - Chestnut - 38"
MUNESS	Wells Sunstar (1638) - Black - 38½"

1958

CLIBBERSWICK	Spook of Marshwood (1632) - Black - 39"
UNGERSTA	Trigger of Marshwood (1526) - Black - 38"
HEOGHS	Starlight of Belmont (1676) - Piebald - 36½"
ORDALE	Lucky Boy of Berry (1696) - Piebald - 40"
WESTING	Hescott of Transy (1661) - Bay - 39"
UYEASOUND	Heatherman of Marshwood (2B) - Brown - 39"
COLVADALE	Wells David (1635) - Black - 38½"
MUNESS	Sprinkle of Marshwood (1611) - Black - 40"

1959

CLIBBERSWICK	Spook of Marshwood (1632) - Black - 39"
	Trigger of Bardister (1703) - Skewbald - 36"
UNGERSTA	Merry Boy of Berry (1626) - Black
HEOGHS	Viking of Houlland (1468) - Skewbald - 40"
ORDALE	Lucky Boy of Berry (1696) - Piebald - 40"
WESTING	Wells David (1635) - Black - 38½"
UYEASOUND	Robin (1607) - Chestnut - 38"
COLVADALE	Lord George of Marshwood (1695) - 36"
MUNESS	Sprinkle of Marshwood (1611) - Black - 40"

1960

CLIBBERSWICK	Robin (1607) - Chestnut - 38"
	Sprinkle of Marshwood (1611) - Black - 40"
UNGERSTA	Merry Boy of Berry (1626) - Black
HEOGHS	Majestic of Lynn (1566) - Black - 38½"
ORDALE	Wells David (1635) - Black - 38½"
WESTING	Terry of Berry (1767) - Skewbald - 38"
UYEASOUND	Spook of Marshwood (1632) - Black - 39"
COLVADALE	Noggin of Luckdon (1698) - Black - 38"
MUNESS	Lucky Boy of Berry (1696) - Piebald - 40"

1961

CLIBBERSWICK	Robin (1607) - Chestnut - 38"
	Sprinkle of Marshwood (1611) - Black - 40"
UNGERSTA	Merry Boy of Berry (1626) - Black
HEOGHS	Lucky Boy of Berry (1696) - Piebald - 40"
ORDALE	Wells David (1635) - Black - 38½"
WESTING	Terry of Berry (1767) - Skewbald - 38"
UYEASOUND	Majestic of Lynn (1566) - Black - 38½"
COLVADALE	Noggin of Luckdon (1698) - Black - 38"
MUNESS	Mighty Fine of Netherley (1459) - Black - 38½"

1962

CLIBBERSWICK	Splash of Marshwood (1743) - Black - 38¾"
	Hurtwood Victor Hugo (1735) - Chestnut - 38½"
UNGERSTA	Robin (1607) - Chestnut - 38"
HEOGHS	Rustic of Marshwood (1762) - Black - 36½"
ORDALE	Spaniard of Marshwood (1484) - Black - 39½"
WESTING	Terry of Berry (1767) - Skewbald - 38"
UYEASOUND	David of Houlland (1835) - Piebald - 39"
COLVADALE	Noggin of Luckdon (1698) - Black - 38"
MUNESS	Vodka of Berry (1833) - Black - 40"

1963

CLIBBERSWICK	Nord of Houlland (1834) - Skewbald - 37"
	Noggin of Luckdon (1698) - Black - 38"
UNGERSTA	Robin (1607) - Chestnut - 38"
HEOGHS	Rustic of Marshwood (1762) - Black - 36½"
ORDALE	Trigger of Bardister (1703) - Skewbald - 36"
WESTING	Hurtwood Victor Hugo (1735) - Chestnut - 38½"
UYEASOUND	Joyful of Mousa (1758) - Black - 34"
COLVADALE	Firedust of Marshwood (1769) - Blue Roan - 36"
MUNESS	Harald of Mousa (1687) - Black - 34½"

1964

CLIBBERSWICK	Nord of Houlland (1834) - Skewbald - 37"
	Noggin of Luckdon (1698) - Black - 38"
UNGERSTA	Lucky Boy of Berry (1696) - Piebald - 40"
HEOGHS	Slacks Mighty Fine (1631) - Black - 39"
ORDALE	Trigger of Bardister (1703) - Skewbald - 36"
WESTING	Hurtwood Victor Hugo (1735) - Chestnut - 38½"
UYEASOUND	Joyful of Mousa (1758) - Black - 34"
COLVADALE	Fireball of Marshwood (1650) - Chestnut - 33½"
MUNESS	Harald of Mousa (1687) - Black - 34½"

1965

CLIBBERSWICK	Vodka of Berry (1833) - Black - 40"
	Terry of Berry (1767) - Skewbald - 38"
UNGERSTA	Lucky Boy of Berry (1696) - Piebald - 40"
HEOGHS	Noggin of Luckdon (1698) - Black - 38"
ORDALE	Neptune of Burragarth (1844) - Black - 34"
WESTING	Trigger of Bardister (1703) - Skewbald - 36"
UYEASOUND	Slacks Mighty Fine (1631) - Black - 39"
COLVADALE	Ballito (1640) - Black - 36"
MUNESS	Nord of Houlland (1834) - Skewbald - 37"

1966

CLIBBERSWICK	Veister of Berry (1932) - Black - 40"
	Moss (1818) - Brown - 38"
UNGERSTA	Lucky Boy of Berry (1696) - Piebald - 40"
HEOGHS	Robin (1607) - Chestnut - 38"
ORDALE	Neptune of Burragarth (1844) - Black - 34"
WESTING	Sprinkle of Marshwood (1611) - Black - 40"
UYEASOUND	Slacks Mighty Fine (1631) - Black - 39"
COLVADALE	Noggin of Luckdon (1698) - Black - 38"
MUNESS	Nord of Houlland (1834) - Skewbald - 37"

1967

CLIBBERSWICK	Leo of Grunivoe (1935) - Skewbald - 37½"
	Little Nipper of Vesquoy (1971) - Black - 36½"
UNGERSTA	Moss (1818) - Brown - 38"
	Superstition of Marshwood (1850) - Black - 38"
HEOGHS	Noggin of Luckdon (1698) - Black - 38"
ORDALE	Norman of Crosbister (1953) - Black - 38"
WESTING	Trigger of Bardister (1703) - Skewbald - 36"
UYEASOUND	Robin (1607) - Chestnut - 38"
COLVADALE	Merry Boy of Berry (1626) - Black
MUNESS	Frisky of Muness ( ) - Black - 36"

1968

CLIBBERSWICK	Little Nipper of Vesquoy (1971) - Black - 36½"
	Leo of Grunivoe (1935) - Skewbald - 37½"
UNGERSTA	Neptune of Burragarth (1844) - Black - 34"
	Florin (1851) - Skewbald - 37"
HEOGHS	Rosetaupe of Transy (2017) - Black - 37"
ORDALE	Sunburn of Marshwood (2025) - Bay - 38"
WESTING	Trigger of Bardister (1703) - Skewbald - 37"
UYEASOUND	Robin (1607) - Chestnut - 38"
COLVADALE	Merry Boy of Berry (1626) - Black
MUNESS	Lucky Boy of Berry (1696) - Piebald - 40"

1969

CLIBBERSWICK	Trigger of Bardister (1703) - Skewbald - 36"
	Norman of Crosbister (1953) - Black - 36"
UNGERSTA	Sunburn of Marshwood (2025) - Bay - 38"
	Little Nipper of Vesquoy (1971) - Black - 36½"
HEOGHS	Rosetaupe of Transy (2017) - Black - 37"
ORDALE	Slacks Mighty Fine (1631) - Black - 39"
WESTING	Harald of Mousa (1687) - Black - 34½"
UYEASOUND	Blackhall Andy (2057) - Black - 36¾"
COLVADALE	Orion of Mousa (1948) - Black - 34½"
MUNESS	Lucky Boy of Berry (1696) - Piebald - 40"

1970

CLIBBERSWICK	Floriston of Hools (2181) - Brown & White - 37"
	Sprite of Marshwood (2280) - Black - 38"
UNGERSTA	Shem of Gue (1982) - Piebald - 36"
	Stellbay of Transy (2288) - Bay - 38"
HEOGHS	Star of Hope (1955) - Grey - 39"
ORDALE	Moss (1818) - Brown - 38"
WESTING	Little Nipper of Vesquoy (1971) - Black - 36½"
UYEASOUND	Rosetaupe of Transy (2017) - Black - 37"
COLVADALE	Orion of Mousa (1948) - Black - 34½"
MUNESS	Spook of Marshwood (1632) - Black - 39"

1971

CLIBBERSWICK	Bard of Marshwood (2530) - Brown - 37"
	Heswick of Transy (2402) - Grey - 37"
UNGERSTA	Hero of Kirkatown (2329) - Black - 36"
	Hope of Housabister (2364) - Skewbald - 37"
HEOGHS	Neptune of Burragarth (1844) - Black - 34"
ORDALE	Moss (1818) - Brown - 38"
WESTING	Norman of Crosbister (1953) - Black - 36"
UYEASOUND	Spree of Marshwood (2013) - Black - 38¾"
COLVADALE	Bard of Crosbister (1953) - Black - 36"
MUNESS	Spook of Marshwood (1632) - Black - 39"

1972

CLIBBERSWICK	Ralph of Tangwick (2156) - Bay - 37"
UNGERSTA	Hero of Kirkatown (2329) - Black - 36"
	Hope of Housabister (2364) - Skewbald - 37"
HEOGHS	Neptune of Burragarth (1844) - Black - 34"
ORDALE	Bard of Marshwood (2530) - Brown - 37"
WESTING	Sunburn of Marshwood (2025) - Bay - 38"
UYEASOUND	Rambler of Berry (1749) - Chestnut - 39"
COLVADALE	Firearm of Marshwood (2528) - Chestnut - 36"
MUNESS	Tuskar of Mousa (2173) - Black - 36½"

1973

CLIBBERSWICK	Vagabond of Berry (1819) - Black - 36½"
UNGERSTA	Splash of Grunivoe (2665) - Piebald - 36"
	Freeman of Marshwood (2526) - Black - 37"
HEOGHS	Garnet of Belmont (2323) - Chestnut - 34½"
ORDALE	Turpin of Gravens (2254) - Black - 33"
WESTING	Speck of Belmont (1979) - Black - 36½"
UYEASOUND	Shem of Gue (1982) - Piebald - 36"
COLVADALE	Olympus of Mousa (1947) - Black - 38"
MUNESS	Surety of Marshwood (2529) - Black - 37"

1974

CLIBBERSWICK	Vagabond of Berry (1819) - Black - 36½"
UNGERSTA	Cardinal of Waterloo (2239) - Chestnut - 38"
	Beberu of Kirkholm (2510) - Black - 34"
HEOGHS	Garnet of Belmont (2323) - Chestnut - 34½"
ORDALE	Sultan of Mousa (2128) - Black - 33½"
WESTING	Sunburn of Marshwood (2025) - Bay - 38"
UYEASOUND	Shem of Gue (1982) - Piebald - 36"
COLVADALE	Turpin of Gravens (2254) - Black - 33"
MUNESS	Splash of Grunivoe (2665) - Piebald - 36"

1975

CLIBBERSWICK	Gedloch Shawn (2658) - Black - 37½"
	Tysak (2784) - Skewald - 37"
UNGERSTA	Cardinal of Waterloo (2239) - Chestnut - 38"
	Zest of Mousa (2796) - Black - 38½"
HEOGHS	Garnet of Belmont (2323) - Chestnut - 34½"
ORDALE	Tiny Tim (2580) - Black - 34"
WESTING	Sunburn of Marshwood (2025) - Bay - 38"
UYEASOUND	Firebrand of Marshwood (2527) - Chestnut - 35½"
COLVADALE	Turpin of Gravens (2254) - Black - 33"
MUNESS	Garnet of Belmont (2323) - Chestnut - 34½"

1976

CLIBBERSWICK	Tysak (2784) - Skewbald - 37"
	Duncan of Crosbister (2631) - Bay - 31"
UNGERSTA	Gletness Rocket (2207) - Chestnut - 35"
HEOGHS	Dandy of Crosbister (1963) - Piebald - 36"
ORDALE	Sultan of Mousa (2128) - Black - 33½"
WESTING	Olympus of Mousa (1947) - Black - 38"
UYEASOUND	Firebrand of Marshwood (2527) - Chestnut - 35½"
MUNESS	Garnet of Belmont (2323) - Chestnut - 34½"

1977

CLIBBERSWICK	Garnet of Belmont (2323) - Chestnut - 34½"
	Duncan of Crosbister (2631) - Bay - 31"
UNGERSTA	Sultan of Mousa (2128) - Black - 33½"
HEOGHS	Dandy of Crosbister (1963) - Piebald - 36"
ORDALE	Gletness Rocket (2207) - Chestnut - 35"
WESTING	Senator of Marshwood (2324) - Black - 35"
UYEASOUND	Starfire of Berry (2695) - Chestnut - 37"
MUNESS	Blitz of Grutness (2713) - Bay - 35"

1978

CLIBBERSWICK	Garnet of Belmont (2323) - Chestnut - 34½"
	Shem of Gue (1982) - Piebald - 36"
UNGERSTA	Sam of Guddon (2430) - Black - 34"
HEOGHS	Duncan of Crosbister (2631) - Bay - 31"
ORDALE	Sherry of Berry (1889) - Chestnut - 37"
WESTING	Ginger of Murrion (2739) - Chestnut - 32"
UYEASOUND	Gletness Red Lamp (2714) - Chestnut - 37½"
MUNESS	Blitz of Grutness (2713) - Bay - 35"

1979

CLIBBERSWICK	Blaze of Foula (2606) - Chestnut - 34½"
	Shem of Gue (1982) - Piebald - 36"
UNGERSTA	Sam of Guddon (2430) - Black - 34"
HEOGHS	Duncan of Crosbister (2631) - Bay - 31"
ORDALE	Sherry of Berry (1889) - Chestnut - 37"
WESTING	Ginger of Murrion (2739) - Chestnut - 32"
UYEASOUND	Gletness Red Lamp (2714) - Chestnut - 37½"
MUNESS	Sultan of Mousa (2128) - Black - 33½ "

1980

CLIBBERSWICK	Blaze of Foula (2606) - Chestnut - 34½"
	Clothie Clett (2889) - Black - 36"
UNGERSTA	Supercharge of Marshwood (2598) - Bay - 38"
HEOGHS	Gletness Red Lamp (2714) - Chestnut - 37½"
ORDALE	Dandy of Crosbister (1963) - Piebald - 36"
WESTING	Duncan of Crosbister (2631) - Bay - 31"
UYEASOUND	Bogs Lucky Bag (2081) - Skewbald - 36"
MUNESS	Sultan of Mousa (2128) - Black - 33½"

1981

CLIBBERSWICK	Star of North Dale (2390) - Grey - 35"
	Clothie Clett (2889) - Black - 36"
UNGERSTA	Supercharge of Marshwood (2598) - Bay - 38"
HEOGHS	Blaze of Foula (2606) - Chestnut - 34½"
ORDALE	Dandy of Crosbister (1963) - Piebald - 36"
WESTING	Duncan of Crosbister (2631) - Bay - 31"
UYEASOUND	Blitz of Grutness (2713) - Bay - 35"
MUNESS	Spangle of Berry (2685) - Skewbald - 36½"

1982

CLIBBERSWICK	Clothie MacFergus (2982) - Blue Roan - 35"
	Richard of Murrion (3145) - Chestnut - 39"
UNGERSTA	Gletness Red Lamp (2714) - Chestnut - 37½"
HEOGHS	Nord of Berry (2694) - Black - 37"
ORDALE	Clothie Falcon (2420) - Blue Roan - 34½"
WESTING	Transy Edel (3293) - Bay - 38"
UYEASOUND	Blitz of Grutness (2713) - Bay - 35"
MUNESS	Supercharge of Marshwood (2598) - Bay - 38"

1983

CLIBBERSWICK	Richard of Murrion (3145) - Chestnut - 39"
UNGERSTA	Rattler of Berry (3372) - Grey & White - 35½"
HEOGHS	Sultan of Mousa (2128) - Black - 33½"
ORDALE	Garnet of Belmont (2323) - Chestnut - 34½"
WESTING	Starfire of Berry (2695) - Chestnut - 37"
MUNESS	Supercharge of Marshwood (2598) - Bay - 38"

1984

CLIBBERSWICK	Gardie Trigger (3375) - Black - 36"
UNGERSTA	Rattler of Berry (3372) - Grey/White - 35½"
HEOGHS	Drum Vampire (3309) - Black - 38"
SOUTH UNST	Gletness Red Lamp (2714) - Chestnut - 37½"

1985

CLIBBERSWICK	Gardie Trigger (3375) - Black - 36"
UNGERSTA	Rustic of Berry (3292) - Skewbald - 37"
HEOGHS	Drum Vampire (3309) - Black - 38"
SOUTH UNST	Rattler of Berry (3372) - Grey/White - 35½"
	Gletness Red Lamp (2714) - Chestnut - 37½"

1986

CLIBBERSWICK	Sport of Berry (3372) - Grey/White - 35½"
UNGERSTA	Wells Triumph (3461) - Black - 37"
HEOGHS	Rustic of Berry (3292) - Skewbald - 37"
SOUTH UNST	Rattler of Berry (3372) - Grey/White - 35½"

1987

CLIBBERSWICK	Starfire of Berry (2695) - Chestnut - 37"
UNGERSTA	Hope of Housabister (2364) - Skewbald - 37"
HEOGHS	Majestic of Quendale (3619) - Bay, black points - 37½"
ORDALE	Clivocast Metaxa (3680) - Bay, black points - 36"
MUNESS	Eric of Quendale - Bay, black points - 34"

1988

CLIBBERSWICK	Starfire of Berry (2695) - Chestnut - 37"
UNGERSTA	Hope of Housabister (2364) - Skewbald - 37"
HEOGHS	Majestic of Quendale (3619) - Bay, black points - 37½"
ORDALE	Clivocast Metaxa (3680) - Bay, black points - 36"
SOUTH UNST	Eric of Quendale (2962) - Bay, black points - 34"

1989

CLIBBERSWICK	Bayanne Prince (3374) - Bay & White - 32"
UNGERSTA	Gardie Trigger (3375) - Black - 36"
HEOGHS	Rattler of Berry (3372) - Grey/ White - 35½"
ORDALE	Hope of Housabister (2364) - Skewbald - 37"
SOUTH UNST	Rollo of Belmont (3971) - Grey/White - 33"

1990

CLIBBERSWICK	Majestic of Quendale (3619) - Bay, black points - 37½"
UNGERSTA	Nixon of Guddon (2846) - Chestnut - 35"
HEOGHS	Rattler of Berry (3372) - Grey/White - 35½"
ORDALE	Hope of Housabister (2364) - Skewbald - 37"
SOUTH UNST	Skerry of Belmont (3606) - Grey/White - 36"

1991

CLIBBERSWICK	Clothie Falcon (3059) - Blue Roan - 34½"
UNGERSTA	Nixon of Guddon (2846) - Chestnut - 35"
HEOGHS	Cowan of Belmont (4103) - Grey Roan - 36"
ORDALE	Jacob of Grunivoe (2299) - Chestnut - 36"
SOUTH UNST	Skerry of Belmont (3606) - Grey/White - 36"

1992

CLIBBERSWICK	Skerry of Belmont (3606) - Grey/White - 36"
UNGERSTA	Noggin of Quendale (3685) - Black - 39"
HEOGHS	Cowan of Belmont (4103) - Grey Roan - 36"
ORDALE	Jacob of Grunivoe (2299) - Chestnut - 36"
SOUTH UNST	Nixon of Guddon (2846) - Chestnut - 35"

1993

CLIBBERSWICK	Skerry of Belmont (3606) - Grey/White - 36"
UNGERSTA	Noggin of Quendale (3685) - Black - 39"
HEOGHS	Tradewind of Clibberswick (3772) - Black - 38"
ORDALE	Jacob of Grunivoe (2299) - Chestnut - 36"
SOUTH UNST	Nixon of Guddon (2846) - Chestnut - 35"

1994

CLIBBERSWICK	Skerry of Belmont (3606) - Grey/White - 36"
UNGERSTA	Majestic of Quendale (3619) - Bay, black points - 37½"
HEOGHS	Tradewind of Clibberswick (3772) - Black - 38"
ORDALE	Victor of Berry (4353) - Skewbald - 37½"
SOUTH UNST	Nixon of Guddon (2846) - Chestnut - 35"

1995

CLIBBERSWICK	Orion of Houll (4338) - Piebald - 35½"
UNGERSTA	Victor of Berry (4353) - Skewbald - 37½"
HEOGHS	Cawa of Berry (4253) - Skewbald - 37½"
ORDALE	Platter of Belmont (3943) - Grey/White - 35½"
SOUTH UNST	Tradewind of Clibberswick (3772) - Black - 38"

1996

CLIBBERSWICK	Thule of Stoorigarth (4164) - Skewbald - 36¼"
UNGERSTA	Drum Rainbow (4176) - Piebald - 38½"
HEOGHS	Cawa of Berry (4253) - Skewbald - 37½"
ORDALE	Platter of Belmont (3943) - Grey/White - 35½"
SOUTH UNST	Tradewind of Clibberswick (3772) - Black - 38"

1997
CLIBBERSWICK	Thule of Stoorigarth (4164) - Skewbald - 36¼"
	Paddy of Quendale (4078) - Black - 38½"
UNGERSTA	Drum Rainbow (4176) - Piebald - 38½"
HEOGHS	Cawa of Berry (4253) - Skewbald - 37½"
ORDALE	Platter of Belmont (3943) - Grey/White - 35½"
SOUTH UNST	Victor of Berry (4353) - Skewbald - 37½"

1998
CLIBBERSWICK	Crackerjack of Berry (S97-99/AD0463) - Piebald - 36"
UNGERSTA	Platter of Belmont (3943) - Grey/White - 35½"
HEOGHS	Cawa of Berry (4253) - Skewbald - 37½"
ORDALE	Gardie Odin (S97-100/AE0747) - Black - 35½"
SOUTH UNST	Viscount of Grutness (AB0528S) - Piebald - 37"

1999
CLIBBERSWICK	Clibberswick Solono (S98-090/AE0542) - Piebald - 34"
UNGERSTA	Thule of Stoorigarth (4164) - Skewbald - 36¼"
HEOGHS	Paddy of Quendale (4078) - Black - 38½"
ORDALE	Gardie Odin (S97-100/AE0474) - Black - 37½"
COLVADALE	
Mares 35" or less	Clivocast Rustic (S97-122/AD05520 - Chestnut - 33½"
MUNESS	
Mares over 35"	Knock Jolly Roger (AC0735) - Chestnut - 39¾"

Fetlar
1956
Viking of Houlland (1468) - Skewbald - 40"
Sprinkle of Marshwood (1611) - Black - 40"
Robin (1607) - Chestnut - 38"

1957
Norseman (1448) - Piebald - 39"
Wells David (1635) - Black - 38½"
Airborne (1426) - Piebald - 39"

1958
Polydor of Holne (1421) - White - 40"
Norseman (1448) - Piebald - 39"
Satellite of Belmont (6B) - Skewbald - 39"

1959
Satellite of Belmont (6B) - Skewbald - 39"
Noggin of Luckdon (1698) - Black - 38"
Berry Coronation (1682) - Black - 41"

1960
Satellite of Belmont (6B) - Skewbald - 39"
Paddy of Troil (5B) - Black - 39"
Viking of Houlland (1468) - Skewbald - 40"

1961	Satellite of Belmont (6B) - Skewbald - 39" Paddy of Troil (5B) - Black - 39" Trigger of Bardister (1703) - Skewbald - 36"
1962	Sprinkle of Marshwood (1611) - Black - 36" Moss (1818) - Brown - 38" Trigger of Bardister (1703) - Skewbald - 36"
1963	Vodka of Berry (1833) - Black - 40" Splash of Marshwood (1743) - Black - 38¾" Sprinkle of Marshwood (1611) - Black - 36"
1964	Vodka of Berry (1833) - Black - 40" Moss (1818) - Brown - 38" Sprinkle of Marshwood (1611) - Black - 36"
1965	Hurtwood Victor Hugo (1735) - Chestnut - 38½" Moss (1818) - Brown - 38" Sprinkle of Marshwood - Black - 36"
1966	Hurtwood Victor Hugo (1735) - Chestnut - 38½" Norman of Crosbister (1953) - Black - 36"
1967	Slacks Mighty Fine (1631) - Black - 39" Nero of Houlland (1590) - Piebald - 36" Hurtwood Victor Hugo (1735) - Chestnut - 38½"
1968	Noggin of Luckdon (1698) - Black - 38" Slacks Mighty Fine (1631) - Black - 39" Norman of Crosbister (1953) - Black - 36"
1969	Neptune of Burragarth (1844) - Black - 34" Donnachaidh Saigean (1645) - Black - 37" Vagabond of Berry (1819) - Black - 36½"
1970	Fireball of Marshwood (1686) - Chestnut - 33½" Neptune of Burragarth (1844) - Black - 34" Lucky Boy of Berry (1696) - Black - 36½"
1971	Lucky Boy of Berry (1696) - Piebald - 40" Rambler of Berry (1749) - Chestnut - 39" Spree of Marshwood (2103) - Black - 38¾"
1972	Dot of Swankitofts (2395) - Chestnut - 37" Orion of Mousa (1948) - Black - 39" Bard of Crosbister (1962) - Piebald - 38"

| 1973 | Dot of Swankitofts (2395) - Chestnut - 37" |
| | Spook of Marshwood (1632) - Black - 39" |

| 1974 | Olympus of Mousa (1947) - Black - 38" |
| | Rob Roy of Greenfield (2625) - Chestnut - 39" |

| 1975 | Olympus of Mousa (1947) - Black - 38" |
| | Splash of Grunivoe (2665) - Piebald - 39" |

| 1976 | Honey Boy of Berry (2929) - Chestnut - 39½" |

| 1977 | Honey Boy of Berry (2929) - Chestnut - 39½" |

| 1978 | Clothie Clett (2889) - Black - 36" |

| 1979 | Clothie Clett (2889) - Black - 36" |

| 1980 | Garnet of Belmont (2323) - Chestnut - 34½" |

| 1981 | Sultan of Mousa (2128) - Black - 33½" |

| 1982 | Rustic of Berry (3292) - Skewbald - 37" |

| 1983 | Bon Bon of Berry (2693) - White - 35" |

| 1984 | Eric of Quendale (2962) - Bay, black points - 34" |

There were no more scheme stallions placed in Fetlar after this.

The Mainland
1956
| ESHANESS | Norseman (1448) - Piebald - 38" |
| WALLS | Trigger of Marshwood (1526) - Black - 38" |

1957
ESHANESS	Viking of Houlland (1468) - Piebald - 40"
WALLS	Gerald of Longhaugh (1496) - Black - 41"
GRUTING	Merry Boy of Berry (1626) - Black
NESTING (West)	Spaniard of Marshwood (1484) - Black - 39½"

1958
ESHANESS	Viking of Houlland (1468) - Piebald - 40"
WALLS	Spritely of Shalloch (1450) - Black - 39"
WALLS (Setter)	Heetam of Berry (1659) - Black - 39½"
GRUTING	Paddy of Troil (5B) - Black - 39"
NESTING (East)	Spaniard of Marshwood (1484) - Black - 39½"
NESTING (West)	Middlethird Ranger (3B) - Black - 36"

1959

ESHANESS	Slacks Mighty Fine (1631) - Black - 39"
WALLS	Spaniard of Marshwood (1484) - Black - 39½"
WALLS (Setter)	Heetam of Berry (1659) - Black - 39½"
GRUTING	Paddy of Troil (5B) - Black - 39"
NESTING (East)	Superior of Marshwood (1633) - Black - 39"
NESTING (West)	Middlethird Ranger (3B) - Black - 36"

1960

ESHANESS	Slacks Mighty Fine (1631) - Black - 39"
WALLS	Spaniard of Marshwood (1484) - Black - 39½"
WALLS (Setter)	Rosald of Transy (1699) - Black - 38½"
GRUTING	Trigger of Bardister (1703) - Skewbald - 36"
NESTING (East)	Superior of Marshwood (1633) - Black - 39"
NESTING (West)	Middlethird Ranger (3B) - Black - 36"

1961

ESHANESS	Slacks Mighty Fine (1631) - Black - 39"
WALLS	Spook of Marshwood (1632) - Black - 39½"
WALLS (Setter)	Slacks Thunderflash (1674) - Chestnut - 37"
GRUTING	Middlethird Ranger (3B) - Black - 36"
NESTING (East)	Superior of Marshwood (1633) - Black - 39"
NESTING (West)	Dragonfly of Marshwood (1685) - Black - 38"

1962

ESHANESS	Slacks Thunderflash (1674) - Chestnut - 37"
WALLS	Lucky Boy of Berry (1696) - Piebald - 40"
WALLS (Setter)	Slacks Mighty Fine (1631) - Black - 39"
GRUTING	Ranger of Houlland (1782) - Skewbald - 39"
NESTING (East)	Dragonfly of Marshwood (1685) - Black - 38"
NESTING (West)	Avening Golden Pippit (1705) - Chestnut - 37"

1963

ESHANESS	Slacks Thunderflash (1674) - Chestnut - 37"
WALLS	Lucky Boy of Berry (1696) - Piebald - 40"
WALLS (Setter)	Slacks Mighty Fine (1631) - Black - 39"
GRUTING	Rosald of Transy (1699) - Black - 38¾"
NESTING (East)	Ballito (1640) - Black - 36"
NESTING (West)	Moss (1818) - Brown - 38"

1964

ESHANESS	Robin (1607) - Chestnut - 38"
WALLS	Majestic of Lynn (1566) - Black - 38½"
WALLS (Setter)	Little Nipper of Vesquoy (1791) - Black - 36½"
GRUTING	Splash of Marshwood (1743) - Black - 38¾"
NESTING (East)	Fireless of Marshwood (1849) - Chestnut - 35½"
NESTING (West)	Slacks Thunderflash (1674) - Chestnut - 37"

1965

ESHANESS	Robin (1607) - Chestnut - 38"
WALLS	Avening Red Robin (1756) - Chestnut - 39"
WALLS (Setter)	Little Nipper of Vesquoy (1791) - Black - 36½"
GRUTING	Merry Boy of Berry (1626) - Black
NESTING (East)	Fireball of Marshwood (1686) - Chestnut - 33½"
NESTING (West)	Harald of Mousa (1687) - Black - 34½"

1966

ESHANESS	Trigger of Bardister (1703) - Skewbald - 36"
WALLS	Vagabond of Berry (1819) - Black - 36½"
WALLS (Setter)	Orion of Mousa (1948) - Black - 39"
GRUTING	Leo of Grunivoe (1953) - Skewbald - 37½"
NESTING (East)	Olympus of Mousa (1947) - Black - 38"
NESTING (West)	Little Nipper of Vesquoy (1791) - Black - 36½"

1967

ESHANESS	Florin (1851) - Skewbald - 37"
WALLS	Vagabond of Berry (1819) - Black - 36½"
WALLS (Setter)	Orion of Mousa (1948) - Black - 39"
GRUTING	Neptune of Burragarth (1844) - Black - 34"
NESTING (East)	Fireball of Marshwood (1686) - Chestnut - 33½"

1968

ESHANESS	Fireball of Marshwood (1686) - Chestnut - 33½"
WALLS	Vagabond of Berry (1819) - Black - 36½"
WALLS (Setter)	Harald of Mousa (1687) - Black - 34½"
GRUTING	Moss (1818) - Brown - 38"
NESTING (East)	Superstition of Marshwood (1850) - Black - 38"

1969

ESHANESS	Fireball of Marshwood (1686) - Chestnut - 33½"
WALLS	Rambler of Berry (1749) - Chestnut - 39"
WALLS (Setter)	Merry Boy of Berry (1626) - Black
GRUTING	Moss (1818) - Brown - 38"
NESTING (East)	Baron of Marshwood (1903) - Black - 36½"

1970

      ESHANESS   Olympus of Mousa (1947) - Black - 38"
           WALLS   Rambler of Berry (1749) - Chestnut - 39"
  WALLS (Setter)   Merry Boy of Berry (1626) - Black
       GRUTING   Speck of Belmont (1979) - Black - 36½"
  NESTING (East)   Gletness Fireman (2101) - Chestnut - 37½"

1971

      ESHANESS   Sunburn of Marshwood (2025) - Bay - 38"
           WALLS   Shem of Gue (1982) - Piebald - 36"
  WALLS (Setter)   Tushkar of Mousa (2713) - Black - 36½"
       GRUTING   Garnet of Belmont (2323) - Chestnut - 34½"
  NESTING (East)   Gletness Fireman (2101) - Chestnut - 37½"

1972

      ESHANESS   Speck of Belmont (1979) - Black - 36½"
           WALLS   Shem of Gue (1982) - Piebald - 36"
  WALLS (Setter)   Spree of Marshwood (2103) - Black - 38¾"
       GRUTING   Garnet of Belmont (2323) - Chestnut - 34½"
  NESTING (East)   Senator of Marshwood (2324) - Black - 35"

1973

      ESHANESS   Rambler of Berry (1749) - Chestnut - 39"
           WALLS   Helmut of Transy (2287) - Black - 36½"
  WALLS (Setter)   Valkyr of Mousa (1454) - Black - 36"
       GRUTING   Tiny Tim (2580) - Black - 34"
  NESTING (East)   Eschonchan Bacchus (1730) - Black - 39"

1974

      ESHANESS   Rambler of Berry (1749) - Chestnut - 39"
           WALLS   Orion of Mousa (1948) - Black - 39"
  WALLS (Setter)   Chieftain of Balintore (1922) - Chestnut - 38"
       GRUTING   Tiny Tim (2580) - Black - 34"
  NESTING (East)   Zed of Mousa (2609) - Black - 38"

1975

      ESHANESS   Shem of Gue (1982) - Piebald - 36"
           WALLS   Dandy of Crosbister (1963) - Piebald - 36"
  WALLS (Setter)   Chieftain of Balintore (1922) - Chestnut - 38"
       GRUTING   Senator of Marshwood (2324) - Black - 35"
  NESTING (East)   Surety of Marshwood (2529) - Black - 37"

1976

ESHANESS	Shem of Gue (1982) - Piebald - 36"
WALLS	Baron of Marshwood (1903) - Black - 36½"
WALLS (Setter)	Dudu of Kirkholm (2837) - Black - 37"
GRUTING	Senator of Marshwood (2324) - Black - 35"
NESTING (East)	Surety of Marshwood (2529) - Black - 37"

1977

ESHANESS	Robin of Troswick (2264) - Black - 34"
WALLS	Baron of Marshwood (1903) - Black - 36½"
WALLS (Setter)	Dudu of Kirkholm (2837) - Black - 37"
GRUTING	Shem of Gue (1982) - Piebald - 36"
NESTING (East)	Robber of Marshwood (2621) - Black - 37"

1978

ESHANESS	Gletness Sunset (2835) - Chestnut - 33"
WALLS	Bogs Lucky Bag (2081) - Skewbald - 36"
WALLS (Setter)	Eric of Quendale (2962) - Bay, black points - 34"
NESTING (East)	Hatari of Kirkholm (3069) - Black - 34"

1979

ESHANESS	Gletness Sunset (2835) - Chestnut - 33"
WALLS	Bogs Lucky Bag (2081) - Skewbald - 36"
WALLS (Setter)	Eric of Quendale (2962) - Bay, black points - 34"
NESTING (East)	Supersede of Marshwood (2524) - Black - 34"

1980

ESHANESS	Nord of Berry (2694) - Black - 37"
WALLS	Ginger of Murrion (2739) - Chestnut - 32"
WALLS (Setter)	Spangle of Berry (2685) - Skewbald - 36½"

1981

ESHANESS	Nord of Berry (2694) - Black - 37"

1982

No stallions put out

1983   WALLS   Rustic of Berry (3292) - Skewbald - 37"

1984

No stallions put out

1985

No stallions put out

1986

No stallions put out

1987
WALLS   Sport of Berry (3160) - Grey/White - 37½"
SOUTH MAINLAND   Rattler of Berry (3372) - Grey/White - 35½"

1988
WALLS   Sport of Berry (3160) - Grey/White - 37½"
SOUTH MAINLAND   Rattler of Berry (3372) - Grey/White - 35½"

1989
WALLS   Sport of Berry (3160) - Grey/White - 37½"
SOUTH MAINLAND   Whitefield Edwin (3373) - Black - 38"

1990
WALLS   Sport of Berry (3160) - Grey/White - 37½"
SOUTH MAINLANDWhitefield Edwin (3373) - Black - 38"

1991
WALLS   Gardie Trigger (3375) - Black - 36"
SOUTH MAINLAND   Starfire of Berry (2695) - Chestnut - 37"

1992   WALLS   Gardie Trigger (3375) - Black - 36"

1993
WALLS   Gardie Trigger (3375) - Black - 36"
SOUTH MAINLAND   Starfire of Berry (2695) - Chestnut - 37"

1994   No stallions put out

1995   No stallions put out

1996   No stallions put out

1997
ESHANESS   Drum Sovereign (AC2757) - Black - 38"
SOUTH MAINLAND   Tradewind of Clibberswick (3772) - Black - 38"

CHAPTER TWELVE

SHETLAND SHOWS

Today we appreciate the part that agricultural shows play in the improvement of stock by giving breeders an "ideal" standard to aim for and pin pointing faults to avoid.

HILLSWICK
I was quite surprised to find in Christopher Sandison's diary that in 1840 he attended a show at Hillswick on the 3rd of November. "There was a show of Fat Cows, Mairs and Foals, Butter, Turnips and Stockings etc, premiums offered for the best." The following year it was held on the 13th of October "I was at Hillswick at a competition show of fat cows etc," so presumably it was an annual event. To organise an agricultural show one hundred and sixty years ago in an isolated area must have been quite a challenge.

LERWICK
The Shetland Agricultural Society held a show of livestock at Lerwick on the 9th of August, 1864. The president of the Society was the Rt. Hon. Earl of Zetland. The Secretary was John Walker who was factor for the Garth Estate. The Members of the Society, seventy in total, and occupiers of small holdings were exempt from

Line up at the Lerwick show, c.1900.   © *Shetland Museum*

paying entry money. Members and exhibitors were also admitted to the showground free of charge. The showground was at that time on the outskirts of Lerwick, near to the site of the present Gilbert Bain Hospital.

At the first show there were three classes for ponies:

- Best pure bred Zetland entire with a first prize of £1.0.0 and second prize of 10/-.
- Best mare (pure Shetland breed) in foal or that has had a foal within eighteen months, and
- Best mare (pure Shetland breed) under three years.

In 1866 the prizes for the pure Zetland entire were increased to first £3.0.0, second £1.0.0 and third 10/-. Another mare class was added for mares under two years and the first prizes for mares was increased to £2.0.0. The level of prize money is astonishing as the first prize for the stallion would have been the equivalent of £200.00 and the first prize for a mare the equivalent of £140.00.

UNST

The Unst Agricultural Society was formed in 1870 and the first Agricultural Show was held that year, mainly for livestock and root vegetables. Classes were advertised by means of large printed posters. In 1873 a ploughing match was added. There were various classes for Shetland ponies.

In 1877 a class for Leicester tups was added to the sheep section. It states that a butter sample should not be less than seven pound weight and a cheese sample not less than four pound weight. After that show "30 gentlemen; the committee, judges, strangers and friends sat down to dinner in the Reading Room with the usual speeches, toasts, etc." It had been a very successful day with large crowds.

In the 1914 schedule a special prize of 10/- was offered in the knitwear section for the best pair of gloves knitted out of pony hair. That particular show was

The Unst Show, c.1900.

cancelled because of the outbreak of war so we do not know if the experiment was repeated.

In the early twenties one of the highlights of the shows was racing cross ponies in gigs. Apparently farmer Craigie and his stallion "Black Prince" were the pair to beat. These shows remained popular but were discontinued in 1939.

In 1948 the SWRI resumed the produce and craft sections but it was not till 1971 (101 years after the first Unst Show) that the Unst Pony Show was started with encouragement and help from Mr & Mrs Cox. In 1978, a sheep section was included so for some years now it has been a full agricultural show. At one point Mr Cox was putting a prospective pony judge in the picture before he set out for Unst: "you know it's not exactly a bowler-hatted affair". It's still not a bowler-hatted affair but it has come a long way since 1971. One of the trophies, The Gardie Cup, competed for annually, was presented to the show before the First World War by the Andersons of Hillswick.

Unst bred ponies doing a display at the 1998 Unst Show.

WALLS
The first Walls Show was held in August 1913. There were six classes for Shetland cattle and all of them well filled. There were ten Shetland bulls entered. In addition there were classes for Shetland ponies, sheep, dogs, poultry, wool and dairy produce. There was a driving and trotting competition and "Go As You Please" for boys under 16.

"Arctic Knight" 1112, bred by Dr J. C. Bowie, champion at Walls Show in 1929.

Judging at Walls Show, c.1914, is Anderson Manson (extreme right), Bertie Manson by his side.

At that time just before World War One there were six agricultural shows in Shetland. Besides Walls there were still shows at Dunrossness, Hillswick, Unst, Yell and Lerwick. The Board of Agriculture for Scotland was very supportive in supplying three quarters of the prize money.

Besides the disruption of the war years the Walls Show has had a continuous run under the same format and continues to go from strength to strength. The recent increase in pony numbers is particularly encouraging.

CUNNINGSBURGH

The Cunningsburgh Show has taken the place of the old Dunrossness Show in catering for the south end of Shetland but, to it's credit, it has always been an "open" show and not confined to one particular district. The show was started in 1935, and for the past forty years it has had a very well attended and successful Shetland pony section. Like the Unst Show it has brought up judges from Scotland and England whenever possible. This of course is a costly business but Shetland Islands Council have been extremely supportive of local shows and in particular have seen the advantages of bringing judges from out with the Islands.

There are now very successful agricultural shows at Voe and Yell but so far their pony sections are small. At Voe there is hardly enough room for a pony ring and in Yell though numbers are on the increase, there are hardly enough ponies for a full blown show. It will be interesting to see if the new European ruling on no more "closed" shows will have any impact on the local situation.

VIKING SHOW

The Viking Show at Tingwall strictly for Shetland ponies has become one of the highlights of the pony year. Being near Lerwick it is accessible to breeders from all over Shetland and is very well attended.

After the Centenary Show in 1990 Helen Thomson saw the merit of an "all Shetland Show" and so in 1991 organised the event. Numbers increased gradually and to ease the pressure on the judge another ring for small ponies was begun in 1998.

CHAPTER THIRTEEN

DEDICATED BREEDERS

Over the years breeders have come and gone, great studs have come and gone but a few of them have left the mark of their breeding policy. The most remarkable was the Marquis of Londonderry, whose ponies and policy have been well documented. He had the motive, the opportunity, the means and the know-how to improve the existing pony stock.

The motive was provided by the coal mines' requirement for strong, slightly smaller ponies. The opportunity was there to buy the best two hundred colts in Shetland and further select from these the best six for stallions. The means was there to rent out the Bressay farm of Maryfield and the Island of Noss. The know-how came from the undoubted expertise of Messrs Robert Brydon and John Meiklejohn. These circumstances conspired together to make "the" success story of the pony world.

The Marquis of Londonderry is given such a high profile that one could be forgiven for thinking he was the first person who had ever bred a decent Shetland pony. Where did he find his first stallions and brood mares?

Marquis of Londonderry's "Laird of Noss" 20.   *© Aberdeen University Library, G. W. Wilson Collection*

There was a saying in the south end of Unst that "Jack" (16), made famous by the Marquis of Londonderry, was a "midderless (meaning orphan) foal belangin' to Robert Spence". There is evidence in the Sandison papers that John Meiklejohn bought several ponies from Robert Spence of Murrister in the early 1870s including a horse for £16, but we'll probably never know the truth. What we do know is that Londonderry stallions were hired to Unst and one was referred to as a "pure 39 inch Shetland stallion" in the early Stud Books.

It is sometimes forgotten also that perhaps the greatest difference of the Londonderry ponies was that they were well fed. They didn't have to compete with the milk cows for survival and more importantly they were fed as foals their first winter so they were less likely to suffer from the weak 'rickety' joints which indicate neglect in youth. The old practice of leaving a foal on its mother for the first winter has often been attacked as poor management but it was often the only hope of bringing a foal through it's first winter. It did, of course, have the effect of either preventing a mare from conceiving or causing it to abort.

The Marquis of Londonderry's legacy of foundation stock for many famous studs has been well recorded. The most notable of these, the South Park stud, Earlshall and Transy are known and respected world-wide. Earlshall and South Park both bought foundation stock from Alexander Sandison previous to the sale at Seaham Harbour. Ponies from this sale also went to Anderson Manson who had taken over the let of the Maryfield farm in Bressay, Francis Gourley from Dumfrieshire and Henry F. Anderton from Vaila.

I would like at this stage to pay tribute to the breeders in Britain and elsewhere who soldiered on during the depression and war years. I would also like to highlight the many breeders in Shetland who kept on their ponies inspite of rock bottom prices and frequent disillusionment. The following report in 1926 shows an all too frequent occurrence.

According to the *Shetland News* of November 1926:

> A crofter in Yell recently sent a Shetland Pony to the Aberdeen market. After freight and other expenses had been paid he received a postal order for 1/6.
> He expressed himself as thankful he had escaped paying a bill.

SOME SHETLAND BREEDERS

An Unst family that has been involved with ponies for generations is the Jamieson family of BELMONT. They have bred many ponies of distinction. "Norge" and "Treasure" spring to mind, also the stallion "Baron of Belmont" who had a distinguished show career in Holland and more recently "Rollo of Belmont", to name but a few.

John Smith of BERRY was involved with ponies in the early years of this century. He became Shetland's main livestock dealer and as such had the opportunity to establish a quality stud. He always had an eye for a good beast, an attribute inherited by both Jim and Eva. Their ponies, in particular their small ones, have competed very successfully in show rings on Mainland Britain. Berry stock occurs in a remarkable percentage of pedigrees.

"Rollo of Belmont".

For several years from 1967 Per Helgen imported ponies by air into Norway direct from Shetland. A DC3 Dakota aircraft could carry 30 - 35, a Curtiss could take 45, and 70 ponies were sent on a DC4. Jim was very involved in organising the ponies at the Shetland end and crowds of people turned out to meet them in Norway. "Vane of Berry" (known there as "Prince") bears the distinction of being the first Shetland pony in the Norwegian Stud Book. Eva has often been called upon in her able capacity as judge.

The late Laurence Bruce of BOTHEN had the distinction of owning a small select stud. His ponies were of such quality that you can still "see" them, "Bluebell's" confirmation, "Beauty's" head, "Rosebelle's" presence. They nearly always came through in the show ring no matter what type the judge preferred.

I found a reference to BRINDISTER in Manson's *Lerwick During the Last Half*

Off to Norway with Curtiss aircraft, c.1970.

"Tofo of Berry" with other ponies from Shetland in Norway.

Century. In 1831 peats were being cut at Brindister for people living in Lerwick. They were taken from there by pony at the charge of 1/- per pony per day.

The Nicolson's have worked for a lifetime in promoting the breed and Bertie served as President of the S.P.S.B.S. from 1984-85. They have established a special

"Bluebell of Bothen" 1234 I.S.

143

"Isla of Brindister".

"Pippa of Burland" (now in Norway). Another good filly out of Sheron and Tic Tac.

place in the small pony world, winning several prestigious awards. The Shetland expeditions, in the mid-eighties, to the sale in Reading proved particularly successful for Brindister with a 1st overall award for a colt out of "Isla of Brindister". This mare has produced outstanding offspring and among her stallions three have been exported to Sweden, Australia and Germany while one of her fillies sold at Reading for 1500 guineas. Bertie has been a discerning judge for many years.

John Jeromson of BURLAND comes from a long line of pony breeders. Many years back their stock was mostly brown but of recent years they have concentrated on small to

144

Southbound with the "Shetland Flyer".

medium chestnuts. They have had some outstanding ponies in the sale ring at Lerwick with exceptional prices.

Helen Thomson has put Shetland ponies from Shetland on the map. She has spent a lifetime training ponies and children in the various skills required to compete in performance classes all over Britain. Their efforts culminating in the prestigious classic performances at Olympia have earned the admiration of local and national audiences and when one considers the logistics of setting out from Shetland with a bunch of ponies, a bunch of lively kids and a vehicle some way past it's sell by date one can only marvel. Helen would be the first to acknowledge the support she has had from various people but Marie Brooker and Pat Renwick in particular, and of course daughter, Rhonas.

Her BROOTHOM stud, run in conjunction with Mrs Brooker, has always been a stud of big fit working ponies. One smaller pony, however, has earned her place time and again. That is "Robin's Brae Winsome" alias "Doodle", a 35 inch skewbald with un-

Leona and "Doodle" with her adopted foals

145

Royal approval for "Doodle" at Olympia.

canny wisdom. This mare adopted two orphan foals one season and on visits to Olympia endeared herself to all who saw her, developing a special affinity with disabled and sick children for whom they raised vast sums of money.

A family that can claim generations of involvement with ponies is the Laurenson family of BRYGARTH. Arthur and Peter's great grandfather Peter Laurenson, who farmed at Gremista, had previously had a visit from the, then, Duke of Edinburgh who apparently was serving as a Midshipman on a warship that visited Lerwick Harbour. He had picked out certain ponies he preferred and later in 1864 came the request from Queen Victoria for three.

The Laurensons have concentrated on skewbalds and their attractive bunch of ponies at Gulberwick has become one of the tourist stops of recent years.

The Andersons of CLIB-BERSWICK have been in-volved with ponies for genera-

An attractive bunch from Brygarth.

tions and have one of the largest studs on Unst. Many of their ponies have come to the forefront at the Unst Show. Several of the family are interested and involved. Jem also has her separate LOANIN stud.

Brian's grandfather T.G. Hunter got telegrams about Shetland ponies in 1909 from the Department of Agriculture, but like many more families with ponies they were first registered in the 1950s.

Clibberswick ponies, "Eastwind " in foreground.

Brian bought the black "Sam of Guddon" 2430 ("Gletness Rocket" and "Jill of Guddon") and he left some good stock. Brian's judging has taken him twice to Australia, including the Sydney Royal Easter Show. He was delighted at the commitment of the Australians. The CLIVOCAST stud has taken on a new lease of life with Peter and Alison going for big quality ponies using established Shetland lines with Marshwood and Southley ponies. A few choice miniatures are also kept. A small stallion "Clivocast Brindi" was recently exported to Switzerland.

Clivocast standards.

Marie Brooker driving "Clothie Gloup" 334G and "Clothie Gluss" 333G.

Marie Brooker began her pony breeding in Shetland and established her CLOTHIE stud with standard ponies of quality. She has carried it on with her usual energy and enthusiasm excelling especially in driving. Her long involvement in council culminated in her becoming President of the S.P.S.B.S. and bringing it safely through a difficult period. Their home at Cothal, Aberdeenshire, has become a home from home for "travelling" pony folk from Shetland.

Foaled on the very edge of the world "Vanity of Foula".
Owner Mr P. Joiner.

On the very "edge of the world" Jim Gear has soldiered on with his stud in FOULA in spite of the added problems of transport. So much in the islands is "weather permitting" but on Foula it is more so. Fortunately daughter Penny shares Jim's enthusiasm at her NORTH HARRIER stud, and they produce some good sound stock.

Bill Spence, with limited space, has always had to be selective for his GARDIE stud

Handsome pair of foals. "Gardie Rumba" and "Gardie Rosebud".

and that has paid off. After a lifetime of dedication Bill has joined the small band of judges in the islands. He is fortunate that the family are keen and involved, which is so important to the future survival of the breed in Shetland.

Myrna Flaws had worked unceasingly for the breed in practice and as secretary to the Shetland Pony Breeders Association. She has special-ised in standard, high quality stock which have been very successful in the show ring over the years. The founda-tion stock at GRUTNESS was basically Mousa. My favourite was the black mare "Lena of Quendale" 12791 (Eschon-chan Bacchus 1730 and Alison of Mousa 9848) an outstanding mare blessed with a perfect head. Fortunately Myrna's daughter Sonja has been smitten as well so bring-ing a third generation into the

Myrna Flaws with "Lena of Quendale" 12791.

breeding fraternity with her LAAWARD stud. Myrna has judged several prestigious shows including the Royal and in Norway 1999 she did the Stallion Assessment.

One of the great characters of the pony scene in Unst was the late Bertie

"Gletness Rocket".

Henderson of MILLBRAE and GUDDON. He bought "Gletness Rocket" 2207 (Fireball of Marshwood 1686 and Rose of Belmont) which appeared to click with the long established mares and produced excellent foals. When Bertie went into the sale ring there was always a buzz of anticipation as prices were likely to soar.

The HOULLAND Stud was founded after the second World War by I.E.M. Sandison, grandson of Alexander Sandison and son of John P. Sandison who was the farmer of A. Sandison's family. With a few choice brood mares he soon gained a reputation for stock of merit. The stud was first handed down to son Dr L.E.S. Sandison then to daughter Miss I.D.J. Sandison. The Houlland stud is included in the Unst land gifted to the National Trust for Scotland.

A breeder who has kept a consistent high standard is Tom Robertson of KNOWE, West Yell. He concentrated especially on piebalds and often his foals came into the prize lists at the Lerwick Sales. For many years he ran "Olympus of Mousa" with his mares and he certainly left his mark.

"Damsel of Houlland" with foal "Gillian".

"Olympus of Mousa" stallion for Knowe stud for some years.

Teaching the next generation – Janice with "Hallstatt Arizona".

The late L.W. (Billy) Jamieson of MUSSELBURGH was especially fond of chestnut ponies so if a good one came up for sale locally he was quite prepared to pay for it. He bought the chestnut stallion "Nixon of Guddon" 2846 ("Gletness Rocket" 2207 and "Eve of Houlland" 6887). Fortunately daughter Janice is upholding the family interest by breeding standard ponies at Musselburgh and small ones at her HALLSTATT stud.

A typical Pinehoulland scene.

For many years the Nicolson family of PINEHOULLAND have concentrated on small ponies, even before it became the fashion. Their forte is small, very sturdy chestnuts of quality that usually do well in the sale ring.

Tom Burgess's QUENDALE stud was unfortunately dispersed in 1994 but it has left its mark. He has a good eye for quality stock and bought only the best. When you breed the best with the best you achieve some outstanding results. He saw the potential of "Eschonchan Bacchus" 1730, and made good use of that fine stallion. He is often called upon in his judging capacity.

Another family that can boast at least three generations of committed breeders is the Burgess family of ROBIN'S BRAE. Over the years they have consistently bred good piebalds and skewbald ponies. Their twins,

A bunch of mares from Quendale stud.

Robin's Brae twins "Pryde" and "Joy" with their foals "Tanis" and "Tamara".

"Robin's Brae Pryde" and "Robin's Brae Joy" have a story of their own for they gave birth to their first offspring within three hours of each other. One of their colts, "Robin's Brae Irvine" under the expert tuition of Mrs Ann Swinscow, has come to the forefront as a special animal in the driving section of Riding for the Disabled. Shetlands are particularly well suited for this role because of their patience and innate wisdom. Lorna has been a judge for many years.

Hestigarth (horse's enclosure) is a suitable name for Lauraine and Allan Manson's house. Lauraine's SWARTHOULL stud has become well known for sturdy piebald and skewbald tinies. We watch with interest now that Allan has been well and truly bitten by the pony bug and concentrating on big ponies has started his own stud using the HESTIGARTH name. Quality big ponies are unfortunately becoming a rare commodity.

David Robertson has been a staunch supporter of the breed in Council and prac-

Lauraine Manson with "Cassie of Burland".

153

"Trondra Malonic".

tically. He is currently Vice President of the S.P.S.B.S. His TRONDRA stud is just outside Lerwick at Gott farm. He has gone for the 32" - 37" scale with an attractive colour range, but never compromising quality in the process. David's mother-in-law Peggy Leask has also been a dedicated breeder since the 60s, and her ponies bear the GOTT prefix.

As far as enthusiasm for the breed is concerned few could match the late Eleanor Hall whose untimely death was a great loss to Shetland's pony breeding fraternity. Her WATERLOO stud was one of excellence and it is a credit to her family that they continue.

These are by no means all the studs involved. It was not possible to include everyone. I apologise for omissions.

Eleanor Hall with "Olive of Knowe" 15517, c.1989.   © *Dennis Coutts*

CHAPTER FOURTEEN

THE FUTURE

From some ten thousand Shetland ponies less than two hundred years ago, based mostly in the islands, to perhaps one hundred thousand world wide today is an amazing expansion. What is more amazing is the fact that over fifty thousand of these are in Holland where they take their breeding very seriously. In Shetland at present there are a total of one thousand Shetland ponies belonging to one hundred and seventy owners. We cannot allow these numbers to fall any further.

It is a wonder indeed that there are any ponies left in Shetland. With so many now bred outside Shetland there is no longer any need to come to the islands for stock. As far as markets are concerned Shetland is at the end of the line. The cost of travelling to the islands is high both by air and sea so unless we can persuade the world's Shetland pony breeders that the islands have something special to offer the future looks bleak indeed.

Shetland can first of all offer a unique experience. The islands may be bleak but they are beautiful and to see the ponies in their natural habitat on the hills is a very worthwhile experience. Somehow they look right, as if they had been there forever. They have become a distinctive tourist attraction, and one sees busloads of folk troop out with cameras poised at the ready. It would be a great advantage and attraction to have a pony centre where people could learn a little about the ponies and their long history.

The second thing the islands can offer is fit ponies. If they were not fit they wouldn't survive here. They have survived the rigours of Shetland winters. They move well because they have had to cover rough ground to look for food and shelter with their particular brand of native cunning. They are well "furnished" because without their winter woollies they would perish.

Because these ponies are healthy and fit with plenty of exercise, foaling problems are few. There is little chance of a mare becoming too fat in Shetland, although in late summer they do put on a firm "ply". (I was going to say autumn but that usually just takes one day here.) The mares, like the native sheep, retain their efficient food conversion rate and ample milk yield which is probably the reason they put on weight so readily on rich pastures.

The Shetland Pony Stud Book Society, as the Mother Stud Book Society under E.U. rules is responsible for the care and future of the breed, but the breeders in the isles also have a role to play and a great responsibility.

First we must retain a reasonable number of ponies in the islands in their natural habitat to preserve all the traits that have made up the pony as it is today – the outcome of thousands of years of natural selection.

We must maintain a pony whose quality is never compromised by colour fads and fashions.

We must retain a reasonable proportion of standard size "usable" animals.

Personally at shows I would like to see division into three size groups ignoring colour entirely, e.g. under 34", 34" - 38" and 38" - 42".

Breeders must be especially diligent in their choice of stallions in the islands to make sure there is no weakness passed on to deter survival in this harsh climate. In 1913 Douglas wrote:

> It is above all, imperative – and especially in the selection of sires – to insist on soundness and vigour of constitution; and this becomes the more imperative the more we shelter the progeny of our stock from the rigour of natural selection, and from such severe tests of endurance as are imposed on race horses.

We would do well to remember his wise words.

These are indeed tall orders, especially when one considers the poor returns financially over the years, but only when Shetland can boast a pony of superior quality will it become the Mecca it deserves for Shetland pony lovers the world over.

Let Smirk and Helen have the last word!

BIBLIOGRAPHY

Ballantyne, John and Smith, Brian – *Shetland Documents 1159 - 1579* – Shetland Islands Council & The Shetland Times Ltd., Lerwick, 1999.

Donaldson, Gordon – *Court Book of Shetland 1615 - 1629* – Shetland Library, Lerwick, 1991

Donaldson, Gordon – *Shetland Life Under Earl Patrick* – Oliver and Boyd, Edinburgh, 1958.

Flinn, Derek – *Travellers in a Bygone Shetland* – Scottish Academic Press, Edinburgh, 1989.

Gifford, Thomas – *An Historical Description of the Zetland Islands* – J. Nichols, Printer to the Society of Antiquaries, 1785.

Goudie, Gilbert (Ed.) – *Diary of the Rev. John Mill 1740 - 1803* – Publications of Scottish History Society, 1889.

Hamilton, J. R. C. – *Excavations at Jarlshof, Shetland* – H.M.S.O., 1956.

Johnson, Robert L. A. – *A Shetland Country Merchant* – Shetland Publishing Company Ltd., 1979.

Manson, Thomas – *Lerwick During the Last Half Century (1867 - 1917)* – T. & J. Manson, Lerwick, 1923.

Radice, Betty & Baldrick, Robert (Eds.) – *Njal's Saga* – Penguin Books, 1960.

Russell, Valerie – *Shetland Ponies* – Whittet Books Ltd., London 1996.

Sandison, Robert – *Christopher Sandison of Eshaness (1781 - 1870) Diarist in an age of Social Change* – The Shetland Times Ltd., Lerwick, 1997.

Sinclair, Sir John – *The Statistical Account of Scotland 1791 - 1799* – E. P. Publishing Ltd., 1978.

Tait, E. S. Reid – *A Lerwick Miscellany* – The Shetland Times Ltd., Lerwick, 1955.

Turner, Val – *Ancient Shetland* – B. T. Batsford, Essex, 1998.

Wainwright, F. T. – *The Northern Isles* – Thomas Nelson & Sons Ltd., 1962.